A Special Calling

A Special Calling

MY LIFE IN ADDICTION TREATMENT AND CARE

R. GORDON BELL
with
STAN SOLOMON

Published in 1989 by
Stoddart Publishing Co. Limited
34 Lesmill Road
Toronto, Canada
M3B 2T6

CANADIAN CATALOGUING IN PUBLICATION DATA

Bell, R. Gordon (Robert Gordon), 1911-
A special calling: my life in addiction
treatment and care

ISBN 0-7737-2203-3

1. Bell, R. Gordon (Robert Gordon), 1911-
2. Physicians – Canada – Biography.
3. Alcoholism – Treatment – Canada. 4. Narcotic
habit – Treatment – Canada. I. Solomon, Stan, 1939-
II. Title.

R464.B44A3 1989 610'.92'4 C89-093438-X

Typeset by Jay Tee Graphics Ltd.
Printed and bound in the United States of America

To my wife, Mary

Contents

Foreword

Dr. R. Gordon Bell has been, and continues to be, a true pioneer in the field of addiction treatment. Not only has he helped thousands of Canadians overcome their addiction problems, but he has also made a special contribution to the well-being of myself, my family, and countless other Americans. In fact, as I discovered, in the early days of addiction treatment on this continent he spent a considerable amount of time in the United States helping Americans develop their own programs. His pioneering work extended far beyond his own country.

I became acquainted with Dr. Bell when I came to the Bell Clinic at Toronto in April 1966 for treatment of my own alcohol problem. My wife Martha accompanied me and benefitted from participating in the lectures and discussions that were part of the treatment program. Thanks to my Bell Clinic experience and the continuing support of Alcoholics Anonymous, I have maintained recovery from my dependence on alcohol. For the past twenty-two years Martha and I, with our four children and their families, have enjoyed a new era of health and happiness.

In 1966, I was pleased to accept Dr. Bell's invitation to become one of the founding members of the board of directors for The Donwood Institute. Martha and I were also glad to be able to assist in the funding of Donwood's first research and evaluation programs.

In June 1967, Martha's father, Harvey S. Firestone, Jr., was admitted to Donwood. In addition to his drinking problem he had other unrelated disabilities requiring specialized care. He remained at Donwood for six months, achieved unbroken freedom from his dependence on alcohol, and became so impressed with the institute's long-term, three-phase program that upon his return to Akron, Ohio, he organized the Donwood Foundation of America. This foundation, which later became the American Association Against Addiction, provided funds for teams of people from several states to come to Toronto for training in the Donwood methods and philosophy.

I have been amazed at the scope of Dr. Bell's efforts over the past forty years in the development of treatment and educational services for alcohol and drug addiction beyond Canada and into the United States. He has either given lectures or conducted seminars in thirty of our fifty states, and often on several occasions. He began in 1949 when he was invited to become a member of the Committee on Alcoholism of the American Association of Industrial Physicians and Surgeons (now the American Occupational Health Association). This was the first medical association in the United States or Canada to have such a committee. A year later Dr. Bell became its chairman, a position he held for seven years. At each annual meeting the committee hammered home the theme that uncontrolled drinking was primarily a treatable health problem rather than an administrative headache, and that involvement in the Fellowship of Alcoholics Anonymous (AA) and/or with treatment in special clinics could point the way to recovery. The publicity generated by the work of this pioneering medical committee resulted in many requests for Dr. Bell to address other organizations throughout the United States.

In the late 1950s the Guest House Treatment Center for alcoholic priests was opened at Lake Orion, Michigan. Dr. Bell was a regular visiting lecturer and discussion leader for this scholarly group of patients from 1957 to 1963.

He became even better known in 1960, when he produced *For Those Who Drink*, one of the early educational films in the field of addiction research and treatment. It was based on the concepts he had developed with the help of his patients. The film was widely used throughout the United States as an adjunct to new treatment and educational services.

In 1972, Harvey Firestone arranged for Dr. Bell to put on seminars for industrial lenders in Detroit, St. Louis, Pittsburgh, Houston, and Los Angeles. One result of this series of seminars was that the U.S. Navy contracted with Donwood to conduct training programs for seventy physicians and health counselors selected to establish fifteen treatment centers for addicted navy personnel. In 1980 the Henry Ford Hospital in Detroit sent representatives to the Donwood Institute for instruction in the development of their Maplegrove Center, which was being set up to treat addictions. Dr. Bell was also involved in fund-raising for Maplegrove by addressing a special luncheon of business leaders in Detroit, arranged by my brother, Benson, who was chairman of the fund-raising drive. The Maplegrove Center opened in February 1981.

For several years Dr. Bell was the lead-off lecturer for the Utah Summer School of Alcohol Studies at Salt Lake City. He followed this up with other lectures at the Rutgers School of Alcohol Studies in New Brunswick, New Jersey. His three-phase treatment program, which uses total-health concepts as the basis for developing a new, rewarding lifestyle, provided general guidelines for a vast assortment of new addiction treatment services in the United States.

On behalf of the thousands of North Americans who have benefitted from your accomplishments, Dr. Bell, we say "Thank you."

William Clay Ford
Vice Chairman of the Board
Ford Motor Company

Acknowledgments

This is a story of my interaction with a great many people who have made a significant contribution to my personal and professional life, and to the values and objectives that have directed our joint effort. Although I had begun to write a similar book on my own several years ago, *A Special Calling* was conceived in a conversation between two Lindas, my daughter and Stan Solomon's wife, who met through their work. As a result, Stan, a professional writer, came out to see me, an agreement was reached, and he undertook to find a publisher. It has been a rewarding experience working with Stan, and I am also pleased to acknowledge the talented contribution of our charming editor, Kathleen Richards, and the competent management of our business affairs by our agent, Matie Molinaro.

My greatest debt of gratitude is to my wife, Mary. Her crucial role in my life and work since our meeting in 1936 is reflected in the theme and content of this book.

I am grateful to my brother, Oliver, for the time-consuming task of searching through my father's diaries for pertinent incidents involving my early life, and for checking the accuracy of my own recollections.

Thanks, too, are due to my daughter, Linda, who has been my chief consultant for the period from 1972 to the present.

I must acknowledge all the alumni who have worked with us and supported our efforts since we opened the doors of our first clinic in 1946, as well as those who have agreed to have their names included in this book. Our patients have been a fascinating, frustrating, exciting, and challenging group of people who have presented us with every conceivable variation of chemical dependency and related physical, psychological, social, and spiritual problem. Although we have helped many of them, there were others with whom we failed. As of January 12, 1989, 23,997 patients had been admitted to the clinics we established, and those of us who have had the privilege of working with them have been immeasurably enriched by the experience. This book is a partial account of that long, rewarding relationship.

INTRODUCTION

Fighting Against Addiction

We are at war! Our enemy is the most threatening global pandemic that has ever confronted mankind. It is addiction, and I have spent the last forty-two years waging my own campaign against it. My respect for its power is only increasing. I have learned a great deal about addiction, often the hard way and from my patients, and I want to share my experiences with you. But first, let me explain why I believe that the insidious, always dangerous addiction to alcohol and various mood-altering drugs is threatening to tear apart the fabric of our society.

Previous pandemics, such as plagues, have involved microorganisms, a threat that has largely disappeared from most parts of the world by the efforts of biological and medical scientists. Instead of microorganisms, however, the addiction pandemic is caused by our overinvolvement with a vast assortment of chemicals capable of producing pleasurable effects, but in increasingly harmful quantities. People vigorously seek out chemicals, and they swallow, inhale, or inject them in amounts that can produce consequences ranging from progressive decline in health and life-expectancy to immediate death. No combined effort by scientists alone can contain this problem.

With previous bacterial or viral pandemics, no large organizations or individuals benefitted and there was no resistance to their control from any segment of society. This is definitely not the case with the current chemical pandemic. Many multinational companies are responsible for the production, distribution, and sale of legitimate chemicals, such as beverage alcohol and tobacco, and prescription drugs. Large criminal organizations provide illegal drugs, such as cocaine, heroin, and marijuana. Efforts to curtail the rapidly expanding use of their products are met with responses ranging from indifference to violent resistance.

Clearly these powerful businesses have much to gain from public consumption of their products. The illicit drug trade is the second-largest industry in the world, with profits exceeded only by those of armaments. The profits from the sale of cocaine, heroin, and marijuana, among other drugs, provide financial benefits for all concerned, down to school-age dealers, beyond anything they could obtain through legitimate enterprises. With the progressive dissolution of traditional guidelines for healthy, socially responsible behavior, the appeal to the pleasures of the moment has become paramount, and the market for all kinds of mood-altering drugs insatiable. As individuals become imprisoned in the compelling egocentric behavior of addiction, they provide an assured market for as long as the addiction is active.

A person's dependency on the powerful effects of addictive drugs can easily result in the intake of stressful amounts, which forces the body to adapt to them by increasing its tolerance for the drug. This can begin a progression from a deliberate desire to repeat these effects, to an uncontrolled and compelling dependence on the substance. This "loss of control" development, which varies from person to person, the amount of chemicals involved, and the quantities used, is associated with the physiological and psychological changes that characterize addiction. The victims of addiction are trapped in a "behavioral cancer," with progressively destructive effects from intoxication, malnutrition, susceptibility to infections, injuries, and cancer, as well as increasing disruption of personal values and family, occupational, and community relationships. As an example, we need only turn to our newspapers or watch on television what havoc has been wreaked in many urban communities today by "crack," a highly addictive derivative of cocaine, which is easily available, comparatively inexpensive, quickly addictive, and potentially lethal.

But how did all these mood-altering substances become so commonplace in this century, and so deadly? I have studied the history of the role of drugs in societies and have discovered that drugs in one form or another are as old as human society. What is different today is that a large number of drugs is readily available to people of all ages, rich or poor. Also, the stresses associated with surviving in many of today's social and work environments make mood-altering substances an attractive alternative to trying to deal effectively with problems as they arise.

Until 200 years ago, all these substances, whether sedative, stimulative, hallucinogenic, or a combination thereof, were obtained from plants. Our distant ancestors almost certainly explored the properties of every root, flower, fruit, and nut in their territory. Those with the more spectacular effects were often incorporated into sacred ceremonies and festivals. Others were used for medicinal purposes, or were anesthetics. In various parts of the world the most important "old-timers" were alcohol, tobacco, opium, cannabis, and cocaine, along with an assortment of other "uppers," "downers," and "all-arounders."

With the dawn of the science of chemistry in the late 1700s, a new era of expansion in our involvement with pleasurable chemicals began. In 1772 Joseph Priestly discovered nitrous oxide (laughing gas), the first of the synthetic depressants. In the first half of the last century morphine and codeine were extracted from opium to provide our great-grandparents with some welcome painkillers, cough remedies, and sedatives. (Morphine, in particular, has caused severe addiction problems ever since.) A lesser form of addiction in those days arose with the discovery of both ether and chloroform, which made surgery much more tolerable than when the only major anesthetic was ethyl alcohol. In the 1850s the hypodermic needle was invented, which produced a whole new dimension in both the use and abuse of chemicals. In the latter half of the 1800s, bromides, chloral hydrate, and paraldehyde were developed and became the first sedative prescription drugs. The unpleasant taste and smell of paraldehyde, however, precluded much chance of its abuse, and dependence on both bromides and chloral hydrate developed in a limited number of users. But during the late 1800s the most significant developments concerning pleasurable chemicals were the extraction of cocaine from coca leaves, the conversion of morphine to heroin in 1898, and the introduction of the cigarette as the favorite route to nicotine addiction. And throughout the entire period alcoholism remained the major addiction problem in the western world.

So, we entered the twentieth century with a cornucopia of potentially hazardous substances to tempt us. And then we began rapidly increasing the choices. During the first twenty-five years of this century the barbiturate drugs were discovered. They made a significant contribution to the treatment of diseases for many years, before they became recognized as an additional addictive hazard, particularly for alcohol addicts who would go from one to the other, and often took the two substances together. The 1930s produced the amphetamines, Benzedrine and Dexedrine, or "speed," demerol, and LSD. Methadone, which can be used to help heroin addicts kick their habit, arrived in the 1940s. Although less potent than heroin, it is also addictive.

All of these chemicals were available when I began trying to understand and treat alcoholics, and I occasionally found patients who were addicted to more than just "the demon rum." In fact, one of my early alcoholic patients had also acquired an addiction to sodium amytal, which was my introduction to the phenomenon of barbiturate dependency.

I was just beginning to understand alcohol and barbiturate addiction when the "tranquilizers" came along in the 1950s to complicate matters. And when a new variety of them, the benzodiazepines, arrived in the 1960s, we had a whole new problem on our hands. Valium, in particular, rapidly achieved a unique popularity and use in many parts of the world as an effective treatment for a wide range of disabilities. Unfortunately, alcoholics and other addicts also discovered the tranquility these drugs brought with them. Because the benzodiazepines are themselves highly addictive, dependency on Valium added to their problems, and to those in the medical profession who tried to treat them.

The drug culture of the 1960s launched an expansion of experimentation with all of the old psychoactive drugs and a never-ending supply of new ones. The chemical "stews" produced problems drug specialists had never seen before. But the next two decades brought with them an explosive increase in the use and abuse of cocaine, heroin, "speed," marijuana, LSD and other hallucinogens, as well as increased use by younger and younger age groups — with devastating results.

The only type of addiction that appears to be declining in the developed world is tobacco smoking. The irrefutable proof of its contribution to lung cancer and heart disease has been widely publicized, and except for teenagers, most people appear to be getting the message. There is also increased peer pressure against smokers. Smoking is not the "in thing" to do. Unfortunately, the same trends are not evident with other addictions.

As we approach the 1990s the picture is truly a frightening one. When I began treating addiction in the 1940s, I had to deal primarily with alcohol, and occasionally barbiturates. Other addictions were far less common. Today the situation is such that our major concerns are cocaine and alcohol, either separately or together and often mixed with various other dependencies. And at Bellwood we have just set up a program for adolescents with addiction problems, because those in trouble are getting younger and younger, seemingly every year.

Addiction in teenagers can happen quickly because they are vulnerable both physiologically and psychologically. In adolescence, bodies are undergoing changes in hormonal and chemical development, with concurrent emotional turbulence. Values and belief systems may be constantly changing and young people may experiment with what feels right for them. Tragically, many of these youths are detouring into chemical abuse and dependence at age twelve, or sometimes even earlier. It is easy for them to find the substances to abuse, but much more difficult for them to break the habit. Cocaine, particularly crack, is readily available to teenagers. What makes this fact even more frightening is that just one experience with crack can lead to dependency.

In spite of all the bad news about increasing drug dependency, I am optimistic about society's ability to defeat this latest pandemic. As a child, I was raised to believe that positive action could overcome negative circumstances. I was also made aware at an early age that concerted community efforts can accomplish much more a lot faster than people working on their own. When events and personal decisions left me wondering about my future, I was able to rely on these philosophies, and to eventually achieve some of the goals I set for myself. I see our global village finally accepting the challenge of addiction, and its various communities taking decisive far-reaching steps together to win the war.

This is not a textbook. It is the story of my experiences with many remarkable people, individuals who helped me over the years achieve whatever success I have enjoyed. It is also about people who have overcome their own problems, despite often overwhelming odds and an apathetic or hostile society, and who have contributed significantly to the overall well-being of their communities.

There are so many tragic stories associated with efforts to treat alcohol and drug addiction that it is helpful to recall some of the more upbeat and humorous situations. There were many times over the years that our patients' antics were highly amusing and brought us down to earth when we were distressed for a particular reason or feeling too proud of ourselves for a job well done. And as long as the staff and patients maintained a sense of humor we had a much better chance of success. I shall never forget the sight of one patient who arrived at our second clinic, Shadow Brook. He was a middle-aged businessman, brought to us by a friend on a hot summer day from a downtown Toronto hotel. The man was quite inebriated and unsteady on his feet, and his condition was hardly exceptional for somebody who was drunk. But his attire was most unusual. He was dressed only in shoes, underwear, and a bowler hat, and he had a hotel telephone draped around his neck. Unfortunately, we had difficulty communicating with him until he sobered up. I have always wondered how he got out of that expensive hotel in his bizarre attire. During those pioneering days of studying addiction we learned a lot from our patients and they never ceased to amaze us with their practical suggestions.

I also vividly remember a man from northern Ontario whom we repeatedly admitted for short but ineffective periods. On one occasion he complained, "I've spent all that damn money, and I can't drink yet!" He was totally unimpressed with our program for learning how to live without alcohol. He wanted his drinking "fixed," and yet he totally rejected sobriety. His behavior reminded us that we had a long way to go in understanding and treating many patients who were locked into their dependence regardless of consequences.

We also had a number of patients in those days who were surprised with the environment at Shadow Brook. One of them had been repeatedly committed and confined to institutions in the United States. After his admission, he carefully examined all the doors and windows and then called together all the other patients to warn them that the place was phony. "We all have to be on guard — the doors and windows aren't even locked!" We have never locked our patients in at any of our clinics.

We also learned in those days that many patients want one final binge before they begin treatment. One man came to the Bell Clinic, which we operated between 1954 and 1967, from the American Midwest. It took him six months to reach us, and along the way he apparently patronized every bar he came across. Needless to say, it took quite a while to "dry" him out.

In 1951 we opened the Willowdale Hospital for women, and one of our first patients made me wonder why I ever left the family farm to pursue a medical career. In fact, some of our most difficult patients have been women, particularly those who, throughout their lives, had all the material things they could ever want handed to them on a silver platter.

We admitted one such spoiled child in her early twenties, the daughter of a wealthy local family. She had been given little opportunity to develop any emotional maturity or socially responsible behavior. A decade later she probably would have become a hippie and experimented with all types of hallucinogenic drugs, but at the time she was addicted to alcohol. When she was first admitted, she was highly intoxicated. At that time we were still treating alcoholic intoxication with an intravenous injection of glucose and small amounts of standard insulin. Our head nurse held the woman's left arm to allow me to inject fifty c.c.s of this mixture, but the patient grabbed my hair with her free hand and proceeded to jerk my head violently up and down while screaming at the top of her lungs. Although I managed the injection, I was quite shaken (literally) by the incident.

During the first decade of our work we were often forced

to treat patients with alcoholic hallucinations and delirium tremens (the D.T.s), during the initial stages of withdrawal, as well as acute intoxication. Fortunately, we were able to obtain special nurses to assist the regular staff with these patients, and several of them became quite skilled at the task. On one occasion we had a patient in such an advanced state of alcoholic addiction that she required two special nurses for several days, in addition to our regular staff. Treatment procedures have improved significantly since then, and there is now no need for a patient to suffer from such symptoms during withdrawal.

One of the special nurses on the evening shift was caring for a male patient who was recovering from withdrawal hallucinations. She had her back to the window and when the patient began to point and mumble, "Faces at the window . . . faces at the window," the nurse thought he was still hallucinating and did her best to reassure him that he was in no danger. The man persisted, however, until she finally turned around and discovered that he had not been hallucinating at all. The verandah roof reached up to a short distance below the window — just the right distance to allow two raccoons to observe our patient's progress.

We have always listened carefully to our patients and in turn we do our best to communicate our philosophy effectively to them. Occasionally one of the patients will remind us that we don't always succeed. When I was running the Donwood Institute we had a sixty-year-old patient who had completed the initial recovery stage of his treatment program. Before he and the rest of his group were discharged their counselor told them about relapses. They were not the end of the world, she explained. In fact, they could be considered learning experiences, in the sense that the patient would then understand better how to avoid further relapses. This man left Donwood shortly after and immediately got thoroughly soused. He had come to the conclusion that the learning experience was a prerequisite for recovery. Fortunately, none of the others in his group misinterpreted the discussion in the same way but we made sure not to make the same mistake again.

I trust that these, and other stories I relate throughout the book, will communicate the positive, caring approach I have always tried to maintain at our clinics. I also hope that our stories will encourage people to become involved in constructive efforts at addiction treatment and prevention. Perhaps our experiences will contribute in some small degree to what I refer to as "Operation Survival."

CHAPTER ONE

A Very Busy Childhood

I doubt if I would ever have become involved in the treatment of addiction problems had it not been for the experiences of my formative years. I grew up in a warm, caring home environment. I was taught to accept responsibilities at an early age and to do my share of the farm and family tasks. It has helped to have been blessed with boundless energy. Sometimes I wonder how I managed to get by with so little sleep in the days when I was trying to become established in my field and raise a family at the same time. But when I think back to my childhood I realize that I was usually much too busy to worry about resting anyway. There have been few dull moments in my life.

I was born on the eleventh day of the seventh month of the eleventh year of this century, which might lead some people to believe that I was born lucky. If that is so, the time of my arrival did not help to ease my entry into the world. According to my father's diary, my introduction to extra-uterine reality was a very stressful experience for everyone concerned. He was not one to waste words.

I grew up near Stratford, Ontario, in a family where strangers were always welcomed, and years later it was only second nature for me to open my own home to people who came to me for help. I used to listen to my maternal grandmother and David Oliver, my great-uncle, relate stories about all the tramps, peddlers, and other transient people who walked the roads in our area. I knew that most of the travelers, regardless of their calling or background, were treated hospitably by both sides of my family. My maternal grandparents even kept an extra bed for overnight guests, the wanderers of the road. Some stayed over more than once; others were never seen again. I recall a man who came in one night in sub-zero weather. Both his feet were frost-bitten, because he was wearing only long leather boots and no socks. But in the morning he just quietly jammed his painfully swollen feet back into his boots and left the house without even waiting for breakfast.

I was surrounded by wonderful relatives — grandparents, uncles, aunts, and cousins. To me, they were warm, friendly people, always willing to help out when needed. At one time or another some of them lived in our farmhouse, so I was never at a loss for companionship.

My parents were both kind and compassionate people, although my mother displayed a wider range of emotional responses to daily events than did my father. Since I was an active, often mischievous child, their mild temperaments saved me from severe punishment on many occasions. My father was a careful, methodical man. (Except when he was hammering nails, that is. His fingernails were often black and blue after such a chore.) He observed my exuberant activities with tolerant amusement most of the time, but he was quite capable of giving me a cuff on the ear and a warning to be less rambunctious when I got out of hand. From the time of his marriage until his death in 1956 at age seventy-seven, he kept a diary, which has been invaluable to me in preparing the recollections of my early years. Father was considered a man of sensible opinions on many subjects. People would occasionally come to him requesting help in writing a speech for a political rally or other community function, and although he did not like making speeches himself, he could express thoughts well in writing. Like some of my other relatives, he had been a school teacher before returning to the family farm to make his living.

Music played a big part in our lives on the farm. Both the Bells and the Olivers boasted some fine musicians and singers in their families, and parties at our home included old-time fiddling, piano playing, and dancing. One of my grandfather Oliver's younger brothers, Charles, had a fine tenor voice. He was also a gifted athlete and a fine medical doctor, and he eventually became one of my role models. After graduation from high school, my uncle Charlie became a school teacher to save money so that he could attend medical school. He graduated from Trinity College medical school in Toronto in 1890. After several years in general practice he went to Rotunda Hospital in Dublin, Ireland, and to other hospitals in London, England, for his postgraduate training in obstetrics. When he finally returned to Canada, he set up practice in Chatham, Ontario. At the time of his death in 1933 at age sixty-seven, he had helped deliver an average of 126 babies per year, believed to be a North American record at the time. His sleep was so consistently interrupted that on more than one occasion he was involved in car accidents when he fell asleep at the wheel.

Religion played a dominant part in the life of the community, and my father made sure that I went to church every Sunday. In fact, I received a diploma for unbroken attendance at Sunday school over a seven-year period, thanks to Father's efforts. For her part, Mother insisted that her three children all take piano lessons. When my music teacher was absent from church I was sometimes called upon to play the organ for the service, a task I dreaded. I was more accustomed to singing bass in the choir than to leading the singing from the organ. This particular instrument had to be pumped with both feet, and once during a hymn I pumped so hard that a vase of flowers on the organ began to rock so violently that my mother thought it would topple over onto my head.

Our farmhouse was about ten miles southwest of Stratford, Ontario, five miles north of the town of St. Marys, in a rural community called Avonbank on the Avon River. The settlers living to the west and immediate north of our farm were primarily Presbyterians of Scottish descent, like the Bells and Olivers. To the east, most of our neighbors were Irish Catholics who were as devout in their faith as the Presbyterians were in theirs. It was of considerable significance that our property was in an area between the Scottish and Irish settlers, as it served to broaden my exposure to different social backgrounds. Although I attended the Protestant church at Avonbank, two miles to the west, the Bell children usually socialized and played with the Catholic kids across the road and to the east. A close relationship has existed between the Bells and two Catholic neighbors, the Rileys and the Teahens, for five generations now. Such friendships were most unusual when I was young, because Catholic and Protestant families were rarely sociable with one another.

Growing up in a farming community was an exciting experience for a child — but it often meant hard work as well. As soon as the three of us were old enough we were assigned an endless succession of duties and responsibilities in accordance with our abilities to carry them out. We were often annoyed when chores interrupted our play, but we were also proud of our contribution to the farm routine. The cold winters could be tough, especially when we had to clean out the barns, and we were always happy when May came, because that was when the cows and their calves were turned out to pasture. This made it a lot more fun for us to clean out the stables during the summer months.

When I was old enough Dad would roust me out of bed at 5:20 A.M. to bring in the cows for milking. The same task awaited me in the late afternoon, when I often had my younger brother, Oliver, for company. I realized when

I was about seven that I had finally "arrived" when Dad taught me how to milk a cow. I began by "stripping out" the last of the milk from the safest old-timer, and progressed until I had the whole cow to myself. I watched the pros as they tried to avoid the slap of the cows' tails, but I can still feel the whacks on my ear from a cow's bony tail as she tried to shoo away the flies. My uncle Ad who owned an adjacent farm, used to protect himself by placing his cap at a precarious angle over his left ear and humming an old gospel hymn to soothe the nervous cow. My mother, however, was not one to take chances; she used binder twine to tie the cow's tail to its right leg. Dad often had Oliver or my young sister Jean hold the cow's tail, if the animal was considered tame enough to tolerate the insult. Since we had twelve to fifteen milking cows, our help was welcome, unless we were caught squirting milk at the cats or for letting the cows step into the pails.

As we grew older we kids became aware of the processes of reproduction among the farmyard animals, and when we were strong enough we helped Dad with the Holstein bull. Dad's bull was typical of the breed — a huge black-and-white brute of sour temperament, and he was manageable only by means of a strong bullstick hooked into his nose ring. Initially I helped out by holding the cow. Later, when I was allowed to handle the bull, I felt a surge of pride at such a promotion of responsibility.

Every season of the year was filled with a wide variety of farm chores, and we were always busy. Moreover, we often helped out on neighboring farms, and I was particularly impressed by the willingness of people to pitch in and help their friends and neighbors — and even strangers. Many years later, when I was developing a comprehensive long-term treatment program for my patients, I recalled my farm days and decided to try to involve the community in which I was operating my clinic. I was pleased to discover that an urban community could be just as caring as a rural one.

I learned another important lesson from those early days

on the farm. Our neighbor, Jim Riley, planted flax in one of his fields. This was a new crop in our part of the country and this particular field became known thereafter as "the flax ground." At harvest time whole families of Indians from the St. Marys area were hired to pull up the flax, tie it into sheaves, and set them up in stooks. During those weeks they erected wigwam-like tents on the field. This was the first time I had seen Indians up close, and this led to a very serious conversation with my mother. She explained to me that there were people of many different colors in the world and that it was important for me to treat everyone the same. Her talk had a profound effect on me; I have never forgotten what she said, and often think of her comments whenever I meet someone of another race or culture for the first time.

Although my family and our neighbors were extremely tolerant people, such was not the case in other parts of the county, as I rudely learned when I began public school. From that time on my life changed dramatically; the transition from an idyllic life at home to the battlefield of No. 9 School in Downie Township was a traumatic experience. My school had a reputation as the most unruly in the entire township. There were fights almost daily, and while I had been accustomed to friendly relationships between Catholics and my Protestant family, this was certainly not the case at No. 9 School.

The children of our Catholic neighbors, the Rileys and the Teahens, were attending the same school, as were the kids of several Orangeman families. There had been intense resistance to the Rileys' transfer to No. 9 School, particularly by one Protestant trustee. This had aggravated tensions between Protestant and Catholic children and as soon as the Riley kids arrived the fights began. In retrospect, I realize that it must have resembled a little Belfast. I did not have to worry about my Irish friends, because they were perfectly capable of looking after themselves. My problem was that I was caught in the middle, although my loyalties were entirely with my friends. As far as the other kids were concerned, I did not belong on either side, so I had a very uncomfortable time.

Easter was a particularly hazardous time to be at school. The tensions, fights, and arguments that had been simmering all during the fall and winter exploded during this period and there was often a brawl between the leaders of the two sides. This usually happened when the teacher of our one-room school went home for lunch. For two weeks each spring, the older Catholic boys had to attend Catechism at the church in St. Marys, and while they were away the Protestant boys roughed up the smaller Catholic kids. When Catechism ended and the bigger boys returned to school, it was time to settle accounts.

Aside from the ongoing religious strife, there was another aspect of my public-school experience that contributed to my growing personal problems. I had no difficulty in learning, but I soon found out that to excel in school was to risk being labeled the teacher's pet. In my senior third class, the equivalent of grade six today, I made the serious mistake of spelling down the entire school, including those in the graduating year. This did nothing to improve my relations with the other students. Despite the ease with which I was able to learn and although I earned good grades, I carried with me into high school a sense of insecurity and inadequacy that affected my behavior for years to come.

I entered high school in 1924, quite glad to be away from Public School No. 9. At last, the intense rivalries, hatreds, and tensions of No. 9 were far behind me. Moreover, at St. Marys Collegiate I was able to renew my acquaintance with a childhood chum, George Birtch, who was about my age and in the same year. We became very close friends, participated in intercollegiate debating contests, took part in plays together, double-dated, and visited each other frequently. Since we spent so much time together and had the same initials, we were eventually dubbed "The GBs." George later went on to become a doctor of divinity in the United Church. We remained close friends, and later he made a significant contribution to my work in the addiction field.

My academic record was fairly good at high school, despite my continued feelings of insecurity. I was fairly adept at French and Latin, and to my great surprise, I once managed to score 100 percent in an analytical geometry test. However, I never studied very hard, and as a result, there was often a wide variation in my marks from one term to the next. I didn't realize then that my inability to develop consistent, sound study habits would cost me dearly when I attempted to get a university degree.

Much of my enthusiasm for learning in those days came from Dr. Neil McMillan Leckie, the minister at our Avonbank church. Sometimes I walked the four miles to his home to discuss a wide variety of topics. Dr. Leckie emphasized the need for me to remain a student for my entire life, and not to be satisfied only with what I learned during my school years. I vividly recall the evenings we spent together discussing the golden rule, and the true meaning of loving your neighbors as you did yourself. He stressed that this meant to love your neighbor as yourself, but no better than yourself. To him, the golden rule prescribed a balanced regard for oneself and others as the basis for productive interaction with people.

I completed high school in 1929, a few weeks before I turned eighteen, but I did not go straight on to university that fall as did George Birtch and many others in my year. My father had asked me to spend at least a year at home to be certain that I preferred an academic life to one on the farm. During that year I became proficient at plowing with our new Fordson tractor, both at home and for some of our neighbors. I was also kept busy with all my other regular farm chores. Socially my sister Jean was just entering her teens and was beginning to pick up the latest dances, which she practised with my brother Oliver and me.

But life at home wasn't all farm chores and dancing. When I had spare time alone I did a great deal of reading, and that, together with my discussions with Dr. Leckie, convinced me that a lifetime of farming was not for me. I kept thinking about my uncle Charlie and how much I admired him, and I realized that I too wanted to become a doctor. I told my parents of my decision, and they agreed that I ought to pursue a career in medicine. So, in the late summer of 1930 I enroled at the University of Toronto's school of medicine.

I quickly discovered that I was hardly prepared for what was to follow.

CHAPTER TWO

Learning The Hard Way

I cannot recall exactly when I first thought about becoming a physician. I do know that I was particularly impressed early on with the fact that three of my mother's uncles were doctors, including my uncle Charlie. I suspect, though, that the illness and deaths in our community during the influenza epidemic of 1918 may have initially focused my interest on the care of the sick. I also had an early and tragic introduction to tuberculosis. My father's oldest sister, Margaret, died of the disease in 1918, and a few years later Mrs. Riley, our close neighbor, died of the bovine variety.

My mother's younger sister, Jessie Oliver, was a deaconess in the United Church and had been engaged in mission work in several communities, particularly in western Canada. During the late 1920s she became interested in helping a number of Armenian boys whose parents had been killed by Ottoman Turks in their undeclared war against Armenian nationalism. She became responsible for finding temporary homes for many of these boys, and she used her relatives to great advantage. As a result, two Armenian kids aged about twelve or thirteen were accepted into our home.

Our family physician, Dr. Tom McInnis, was visiting our house one day while the second boy was there. When he happened to overhear the boy coughing, he told my mother at once that she had to have him removed to hospital as soon as possible. By then he had developed such an advanced case of bilateral pulmonary tuberculosis that he died in a sanitarium in London, Ontario, a few months later. Our family had to have TB tests and although we all tested positive, none of us developed the disease. There were other illnesses in the family that helped me decide that I wanted to be a doctor. My cousin, John Bell, had nearly died from appendicitis, and his brother Alex had a wasted leg as a result of contracting poliomyelitis as a child.

So, with my uncle Charlie as a role model and my high-school days now behind me, in 1930 I enroled at Victoria College, University of Toronto, in biological and medical science. Although I had a definite goal to pursue, my first university experience was hardly a success. I seemed to be far more promising in outside activities than I was in my education, probably because I did not then have the discipline required for such advanced studies.

During the late 1920s one of the most popular annual events in many towns and small cities throughout Canada was the yearly show put on by the Canadian Chautauqua. The Chautauqua movement began as an adult-education institute in 1874 at Chautauqua Lake, New York state. It was founded by John H. Vincent, a Methodist Sunday-school official, and Lewis Miller, a manufacturer, to "utilize the general demand for summer rest by uniting daily study with healthful recreation." It developed correspondence courses, as well as large summer facilities at Chautauqua Lake. In 1924, at its height, it was estimated that a third of the American population had had some contact with Chautauqua programs. The traveling Chautauquas were a commercial offshoot of the movement, which in the summer months offered three- to seven-day-program packages in circus tents in small towns and villages across the

United States, and later in Canada. Their roots were overtly evangelical, with an emphasis on popular lectures, music, drama, and religious orations.

I had been very interested in the Chautauqua program when it came to St. Marys, but I was even more interested in getting a job as a crewman as soon as I became a university student. Soon, I had applied to work with the set-up boss raising and lowering the large tents that could seat up to 500 people. At first, a Mrs. Erikson, who was in charge of the Ontario operation, was reluctant to hire me, since I was two or three years younger than most of the students they hired for those positions. The job involved swinging a sledgehammer and pounding in pegs to support the huge tent. But when she was convinced that I was in good physical condition and could lay claim to some skill in pounding down farm fence-posts, I was chosen as a member of one of five crews hired for the summer of 1931 in Ontario. Each crew traveled to ten towns in the province for the season.

After the last show in each town, our job was to take down the tent, roll it up, and load it onto the truck, along with all the other equipment — chains, stage lights, ticket booth, etc. At the next town we would start all over again and be ready for the first program on the following day. It was hard work, but I enjoyed every minute of it because I got to travel around Ontario and I met many interesting people.

The advent of talking moving-pictures and the economic crash of 1929 spelled the end for the Canadian Chautauqua, and in the summer of 1932 I found myself seeking other employment. It was the height of the Depression, and jobs were hard to find, so I decided to try sales. I went with a school friend, Leslie Jessop, to the Imperial Publishing Company on Queen Street in Toronto, and applied as a book salesman. The company was hiring students to sell copies of one of their books, *People's Home Library*, in a single volume for $7.50, or in three separate volumes for $9.00. One volume dealt with home remedies, another with remedies for livestock, and a third with home economics, recipes, and other household essentials. Les and I were both hired, and were assigned adjoining territories in Quebec, he to Chateauguay County, and I to Huntingdon County. Huntingdon County is located in the Eastern Townships, along the U.S. border, and across the St. Lawrence River from Ontario's Glengarry County. It was a farming community, consisting for the most part of people of Scottish descent and a few French-Canadian farmers.

I had ordered a bicycle through Eaton's mail-order catalogue, to be delivered to me in the town of Huntingdon. In the meantime, I hitchhiked there with my sales kit and suitcase, and rented a room in town with a Mrs. Dawson, whose son was about my age. He was very skeptical about my prospects of selling anything to anybody. Considering his remarks and the economic climate in the early 1930s, I too was a little dubious of my prospects, as I claimed my bicycle and set out along the highway between Huntingdon and Malone, New York, to make my first calls. I was so nervous before seeing my first potential customers, that I rode back and forth past their driveway several times before I mustered up the courage to go in. Although they didn't buy any books, they did receive me very kindly and invited me to share a very hearty meal with them. This experience was a harbinger of things to come and reminded me of the way we treated strangers at home. During the entire summer, I had to pay for only one night's lodging and one meal while I was on the road, thanks to the warmth and hospitality in that community. I was usually offered more places to stay and more meals than I could possibly accept, and I returned to my rented room in Huntingdon only on weekends to pick up my mail and get fresh laundry.

I was also helped in my budding sales career by my experience doing the farm chores. If I happened to arrive at a farm at milking time, I automatically pitched in. It was the natural thing for me to do because we always helped our neighbors in our own community. Once, in the middle of the haying season, I went into a farmer's barn and could hear someone spreading the hay piles up in the center of the hayloft. I had seen two wagons being loaded out in the fields, so I found a pitchfork, climbed into the loft on the other side of the big mound, and without a word began to spread the hay on my side. When the mound was sufficiently lowered to permit the two of us to see each other, the farmer looked at me in astonishment and said, "Who the hell are you?" Between us, we leveled the hay before the first of the wagons came in, so we had time to examine my wares together. We sat on a beam, I showed him the book, and he bought a copy before the wagon arrived.

After each sale I made, my new customers agreed that I could list their names in the back of my prospectus to show to other potential customers. A few of them told me that if I could somehow get a farmer named John Boldovitch's name on that list, I would be able to sell my books to anybody else in the county. I was warned that Boldovitch was a very tough customer and seldom bought anything from anyone unless he absolutely needed it. When I visited him and began my pitch, he interrupted me by saying that he was not the least bit interested. At that moment, one of his sons entered the driveway with a fine-looking team of Belgian horses. When I complimented him on the team, John remarked, "I used to have a better one, but one of the horses died of colic." (Colic is a condition characterized by acute abdominal pain, often caused by the accumulation of gas and bowel distension.) When I asked him why he hadn't called the veterinarian, he replied that he had done so. The vet had come out from Huntingdon and "tapped" the horse, but it had died. I asked him to show me where the knife had been inserted through the horse's intestinal wall to allow the gas to escape. In answer, he pointed to a spot high up on his horse's left side, just in front of the hip.

"It's no wonder your horse died," I said. I opened my book and showed him a photograph of a famous American veterinarian tapping a horse with colic halfway down its *right* side. I showed him that it was cows, sheep, and goats that were tapped high up on the left, and added, "It would have been safer for you to have boiled your jackknife for a few minutes to sterilize it, inserted the small blade in the right location, and tapped the horse yourself." When he stopped swearing, I asked him how much the horse had been worth. "Several hundred dollars," he replied. "Well," I said, "what do you want to do? Take a chance on losing another horse worth several hundred dollars, or buy this book for seven-fifty?" To the amazement of all who heard about it, John Boldovitch bought the book.

When it came time to deliver the books I had sold, my parents, my aunt Jessie (who had been involved in bringing the Armenian boys to our home), and my sister Jean came down in the family car to help me. Some of the families were unable to pay cash for their books, so we happily accepted maple syrup instead. As a result, I found myself selling maple syrup in Toronto as an extracurricular sideline for one term at university. Regardless of how we were paid, however, Les Jessop and I had the best record of any of the salesmen for Imperial Publishing that summer. Unfortunately, my academic achievements that year were just the opposite.

In spite of my reasonably successful activities during the summer months, the period from 1930 to 1935, when I was aged nineteen to twenty-four, stands out as the most difficult and unhappy years of my entire life. (It also marked the beginning of my smoking, an addiction I tried twice to give up before I succeeded in 1962. In my younger days I had no idea how deleterious the habit was, nor how difficult a habit it would be to break.)

My academic performance was consistently poor for various reasons, not the least of which was that I was not emotionally ready for the self-discipline required for the honors course in biological and medical science. In fact, I barely scraped through the first three years of university. So, in the summer of 1934 I decided to make a killing raising and selling frogs. They were being used in my physiology classes for experiments relating to nerve function. I was curious where the frogs were acquired and learned that they were bought from one supplier somewhere in Quebec and another in Chicago. The department of physiology eventually agreed to purchase their frogs from me if I could supply healthy leopard frogs, two-and-a-half inches long. I decided to explore the Quebec connection to determine how their frogs were raised.

After hitchhiking to the Eastern Townships, I was unable to find the exact address of the university's frog supplier. I struck up a conversation with a young chap about my age who was one of the legions of unemployed at that time. He too was reluctant to help me find the frog supplier until in desperation, I asked him, "Do you like to drink wine?" Luckily he did, so I bought a bottle of wine and made sure he drank most of it. In retrospect, it was probably the first time I tested the persuasive power of alcoholic beverages. As my new friend became more congenial, he decided to take me to the family who sold the frogs. Unfortunately, they proved to be uncooperative, and would not show me how they raised their lab animals.

Hitchhiking home, I was picked up by a French-Canadian Jesuit priest. We talked about a lot of things, but I'll never forget his response when I thanked him for the ride. In his careful, precise English, he said, "It has been a privilege to have been of service." His words made a powerful impression on me — the idea of serving others was not just a duty or a moral obligation, but a *privilege*. This phrase later became the motto for The Donwood Institute. It made me think of my earlier conversations with Reverend Neil McMillan Leckie, and about the similarity between the two men of the cloth.

After I got back to the farm, I decided to hitchhike to Chicago, because I was still eager to find out how frogs were handled after they were caught. I located the company that provided laboratory animals to the universities and discovered that they kept their thousands of frogs in a cool, dark place with continuous running water over the floor. Now I figured I knew how to set up my own operation.

I stayed close to home for most of that summer, selling books to schools, hiring myself out to work at different farms, and organizing young people in the area to catch frogs for me. My father allowed me to clean out one of the box stalls in the horse stable and to install water pipes to supply running water for our frogs continuously over the floor. Our only concern was that we did not know how much water we could afford to divert for the frogs; the horses, cattle, and the rest of the livestock required their own steady supply as well. There were many poor families in our area that year, and word spread quickly that I would pay twenty-five cents a dozen for leopard frogs two-and-a-half inches long. Families living near streams and rivers for miles around were soon catching frogs, and by the fall of that year we had at least one full shipment for the University of Toronto. I was paid a dollar a dozen and for several years afterward was referred to as "the frog man."

In the winter of 1934 I fell in love with a charming young lady named Sally Gillies, who worked for the T. Eaton Company in Toronto. Sally had a great sense of humor and was always able to make me see the lighter side of my troubles. She visited our farm the next summer and was immediately a big hit with my family and friends. I, in turn, spent several weekends with her and her parents at their home in Fort Erie, Ontario, where I was accepted with equal warmth. Sally made a great impact on my study habits, although I was too far behind to pass my final exams in my fourth year of school. However, when I returned to university that fall I was able to enrol in the third year of the medical course again and my studies began to progress satisfactorily. Sally was a steadying influence on my life, and she refused to allow me to spend too much time with her at the expense of my school work.

By the time I went home for the Christmas holidays that year, Sally did not look well. She was pale and was very tired, and at first I thought she was probably worn out from working long hours during the pre-Christmas rush at the department store. During the week between Christmas and New Year's I received a telephone call from her roommate, who informed me that Sally was in Toronto General Hospital with pneumonia. I immediately returned to Toronto, and her parents and I stayed with her nearly twenty-four hours a day.

Sally was confined to an oxygen tent and the doctors told us that her prognosis was very bad. In those days, just before the all-important discoveries of the sulfa drugs, and later penicillin, treatment for pneumonia was largely restricted to relieving the symptoms. Because there was no treatment for the disease, we all knew there was little hope for her recovery.

On January 6, 1935, Sally died. I was devastated. I could not apply myself to my studies at all that term, and I failed my year once again. Utterly depressed, defeated, and ashamed, I returned to the family farm and for the next year I was like a rudderless ship. I helped out where I could on the farm and tried to keep myself busy. I could only hope that I would eventually regain my enthusiasm and return to my medical studies.

Although I had failed third-year medicine, my report included permission to try again. I considered the option and decided that I was not ready to return to school; I decided that I had to accomplish something on my own first, and then assume total responsibility for all the costs of furthering my education. I sought work in Sudbury, where a cousin, John Bell, was a mining engineer with the International Nickel Company. I had hoped to be able to get a job in the mines or the smelter, but there was such a large number of applicants for work with the company that I knew I had little chance of being hired. I had very little money but I traveled to Sudbury anyway and used most of my remaining funds to rent a room for two weeks.

I was too proud to let on to my cousin that I was broke, and after going without food for a day, I decided to pawn my Parker pen. I got seventy-five cents for it and promptly spent the entire amount in a restaurant that catered to the miners, where the food was plentiful if not fancy. I stuffed myself, became violently ill, and lost it all. Now I was back where I started — minus the fountain pen. I hated the thought of having to go back to the farm with nothing to show for my efforts, so I reasoned that until I could think of something else to do, the best way to avoid being hungry was to do as little as possible. For a couple of days I stayed in my room. Starvation loomed. Then, toward the end of the second day, my landlady knocked on the door, came in, and looked at me very sternly.

"Young man," she said, "when did you eat last?"

When I told her, she scolded me and, pointing to the door, ordered me to get down to the kitchen at once.

She fed me an excellent meal and followed it with a sound lecture. "Look," she said, "there are no jobs here in Sudbury. You are not going to accomplish anything by starving yourself to death, so here is a box lunch. You start hitchhiking back to Toronto right away!"

Dispirited and at a loss for what else to do, I followed her advice and returned home. That fall I again plowed the fields for my father and hired myself out to the neighbors to do their plowing and any other odd jobs I could get. Gradually I came to appreciate my quiet time at home with the family and the opportunity to participate in some of the local social activities. Nevertheless, that winter was a long one, as I debated what to do next. I had reached rock bottom and had to find a way to begin a new life.

I was still looking for a job in the spring of 1936 when I received a call from Douglas Weaver, my former roommate at the University of Toronto, who was working for the Canada Furnace Company in Port Colborne, Ontario. Doug told me that the International Nickel Company was enlarging their operations there and was hiring new people. I set out for Port Colborne on June 2. Apparently Inco had contracted with the Fraser and Brace Construction Company to build new facilities for its plant. Inco hired people for the construction company on the understanding that the company could transfer selected employees to the Inco operation as the need arose. I was delighted to be told to report for work at Fraser and Brace a month later.

For my first assignment I joined a gang digging out the muck in a swampy area for the foundation of new oil-storage tanks. The summer of 1936 was one of the hottest of this century, and I was fortunate to be able to hold up my end of the workload, especially because at the slightest hint of shirking the tough old foreman fired any employee on the spot. Four days later I was a little worried to notice him pointing me out to a young Inco official. I was called out to meet the man, and was pleasantly surprised to learn that I was to be transferred to their nickel plant to help conduct some tests on new equipment. The salary at Fraser and Brace had been thirty-five cents an hour for a ten-hour work day, six days a week. Inco paid forty-one cents an hour but for an eight-hour day, so I was actually making less money per day. The "promotion," therefore, was not without its initial disadvantages.

The day I started my new job at Inco, July 6, 1936, became one of the most important days of my life for another reason. When I learned of my promotion, I rushed over to see Doug Weaver. I burst into the middle of a dinner party he was holding for some friends. Among his guests was a startlingly attractive blonde who literally stopped me in my tracks. Her name was Mary Irene Lamping, the twenty-two-year-old private secretary of the president of the Canada Furnace Company. I had little opportunity to say more than hello, but I soon called Doug to find out more about this beautiful friend of his. He advised me not to get my hopes too high, because he was sure that she was seriously involved with a successful businessman from Buffalo. When I did manage to phone and ask her for a date, she declined gracefully, and said,

"Call me in October." I was puzzled. Although there was indeed a boyfriend in Buffalo, I had no intention of waiting three months to call her back. Long before then we were seeing each other on a regular basis.

Once the testing project was completed, I was transferred to assist at the calciner furnaces, where nickel sulphide was converted to nickel oxide or calcine. I had thought that the work on the farm, wielding a sledgehammer for the Chautauqua, and then working for Fraser and Brace had prepared me for any kind of physical labor. Little did I know! The task of filling those buckets of nickel sulphide and moving them to the calciner furnaces four times a shift demanded a level of physical effort beyond anything I had ever experienced. Over the first few days I drank too much water, then took too many salt pills, but finally I began to adapt. Eventually I felt able to hold my own with the furnace men. In 1936 we were required to work 365 days a year, and were paid time-and-a-half on Christmas Day and the first of July. The only time we had off was every three weeks when we came off the midnight-to-8:00-A.M. shift on Sunday morning and did not return to work until four o'clock on Monday afternoon. I had trouble the first few months establishing any real friendships with the older workers, almost all of whom were recent immigrants from Russia, Poland, Czechoslovakia, Yugoslavia, France, and Italy. But I knew I was finally accepted when I received the same kind of kidding as the others, both at work and in the change house before going home.

Mary Lamping had a Chevrolet convertible, the only one of its kind in Port Colborne, and an assortment of men and women friends. Through her I began to acquire a new circle of acquaintances beyond my friends at Inco. We both loved to dance, and took every opportunity to do so at Crystal Beach, Morgan's Point, or some of the other resort areas on Lake Erie and in Buffalo. I discussed any problems I had at the Inco plant with her, and she became a part of my life from that time on.

I worked continuously seven days a week, although I

finally managed to get a few days off during one Christmas/New Year's holiday season. I went home to Avonbank, and my mother was so shocked by my scrawny appearance that she made me get on the scales. I weighed 145 pounds, about fifteen less than when I had started working at Inco. Mother was convinced I could not possibly be eating properly, so she sent Jean back with me to Port Colborne. By this time I had met another young chap in Port Colborne, who was the manager of the local Stedman's department store, and we had set up a small apartment together. I thought we were both eating fairly well. Jean cooked for us, however, and I found a room for her in the same building. Mother seemed to have difficulty accepting that with the heavy furnace work, meals of any size had little effect on my weight.

In 1937 there were significant changes at Inco. Everybody in the plant was given one day off per week. This meant a sudden increase in personnel, dramatic changes in time schedules, and promotions for experienced people throughout the plant. I was selected to be an operator on a new type of furnace — a Mond reducer — which reduced nickel oxide to pure nickel, but I was puzzled when I realized I was having more problems doing my job than the other new appointees. Apparently I was not given sufficient instruction, since someone's friend was hoping to take over my position. With extra work and the help of a friendly subforeman, however, I received all the training I needed to do a decent job. This was a major turning point in my work at Inco (and indirectly in my plans to return to university).

My work improved, and reports on my abilities improved accordingly. By working on different shifts, I became acquainted with and accepted by even more of my coworkers. Many of the men discussed a wide assortment of topics and problems with me, particularly on the midnight-to-8:00-A.M. shift when the foreman or subforeman might be taking a quiet snooze in the office. I in turn discussed them with Mary, and came back with a recommendation whenever I could. Gradually I found that I had won the trust and confidence of many of the tough, experienced furnace men. "Little" Joe La Capria, a fireman on one of the calciners, was a very tough, smart worker of small physical stature, and he treated me like a son. He warned me about all the hazards of my job. He was also interested in my plans to return to medical school in Toronto. If I came to work after having been out with Mary, Joe always knew that I had not had enough sleep. He would always ask, "What did you do last night?" When I told him I was out with my girlfriend at a nightclub in Buffalo, he would say, "Goddamm fool you! Wasting your money; you not watch out, you not get to university."

Joe was very proud of his three stepdaughters, all of whom were going to school. One night he told me that his eldest, who wanted to become a teacher, was having trouble with her high-school course in analytical geometry. As this was the only subject in high school in which I once had a perfect score, I asked him to bring her homework to me to see if I could help. I went over it during my break, laid out some study plans, and sent my recommendations back to her. The young girl passed her final examination in the subject and my friend Joe was forever grateful.

By this time Mary and I were discussing marriage very seriously. However, several situations had to be straightened out first. I told her that I would have to give my medical training top priority, and suggested that we should postpone getting married until after I had graduated.

She would have no part of that. "Oh no," she exclaimed. "I'm not turning you loose in Toronto with all those university girls!" She announced that she would look after our living expenses if I would look after the tuition, and that we would get married before I went back to university.

Mary and her family were Catholics, and one of the conditions of our getting married was that our children would be raised as Catholics. I readily agreed to this, and I was pleased and proud when my own family and other close relatives readily accepted Mary and fully supported our plans. (Only a couple of our more distant relatives were shocked that I would marry outside the Protestant faith.) The only other objection came from Joe La Capria. When he found out I was engaged, he literally exploded in anger. However, he was somewhat mollified when I explained to him the arrangements Mary and I had made to cover our living expenses and tuition, and finally he too gave us his blessing.

After my experiences at Inco, I felt thoroughly confident of my ability to cope with any obstacles in my path. As I looked ahead to my impending marriage and eventual return to medical school, I knew that I had turned the corner.

CHAPTER THREE

Success At Last

Mary and I were married on June 18, 1938, in St. Michael's Chapel in Fort Erie. After a reception at the Black Horse Inn we took off for a one-week honeymoon in the United States, our ultimate destination being Kentucky. I had arranged to borrow my father's car and on the way we visited Huntington, West Virginia, where Inco had a large refinery, and I was able to see how operations were carried out at that plant. This may not have been the most exciting place for Mary to visit on her honeymoon, but she was always keenly interested in anything I was working on, and she enjoyed the plant tour. My main recollection is that the heat at the West Virginia plant was even worse than it was in Port Colborne, and I was thankful that I did not have to work there.

By the fall of 1938 Inco had made significant improvements in the work situation at our plant. A new hall and entertainment center had been built just outside the entrance gates to the plant, and soon after it opened some people in the office decided that the staff would put on a minstrel show. A choir consisting of office staff with the traditional black faces would be responsible for most of the program, with an old-time orchestra composed of workers in the plant accompanying them. I ended up with a double assignment — to sing as a member of the choir and to direct the orchestra.

Workers from all parts of the plant were notified of the plan, and those who could play a musical instrument were asked to attend a preliminary meeting in the new hall. Many of the workers it turned out could play instruments by ear, and a few could even read music, but the wide diversity of their backgrounds and cultures meant that few of them knew the same tunes. I finally selected about ten or eleven men who I felt could be trained to play the same tune together, and our practice sessions began with me at the piano. We had to rehearse in off-hours, but no one seemed to mind, as we became friendly enough to engage in rough, humorous kidding about a variety of styles and skills.

We had two fiddlers, a guitar player, a banjo player, a drummer, an accordionist, a man who played the mouth organ, and a few more. I finally got them to harmonize on three numbers, the main one being a fiddler's tune I had learned back home called, "The Wind that Shakes the Barley," which they all seemed to learn quickly. The trouble with the band was not getting them started, but getting them to stop at the same time. Many of them were used to playing for old-time dances at which they would repeat a number over and over again, and they had trouble breaking this habit. At last we decided that when we came around for the final time I would call out "Whoa!" just as I did to halt the horses back home on the farm. The signal worked very well for the concert we put on in Port Colborne; in fact, the whole performance was so successful that we were soon invited to repeat it in Welland a few miles away.

My "orchestra" had two places on the Welland musical program, one near the beginning of the evening and the other toward the end. Many of my players were nervous about this extra assignment in another town, afraid that they would make a mistake or somehow make fools of themselves. I was therefore surprised and pleased to find them quite relaxed during their first number. They played with vigor and flair, and received thunderous applause.

When the men came on stage for the second set, however, it was immediately obvious that something unusual had happened during the intermission. They were joking among themselves, seemed happier and more relaxed, and they played with even greater gusto than before. When I tried to get them to stop by yelling "Whoa!" two or three of them stopped and walked off the stage, but the rest kept on playing. Next time around I yelled "Whoa!" again, and a few more left the stage while the others played on. By this time the audience was roaring with laughter, and I was trying to figure out what was happening. The third time, I roared out my "Whoa!" so loudly that it must have been heard out on the street. This time the remaining orchestra members obediently stopped, albeit reluctantly, and stomped off the stage. The audience was in stitches over the entire performance.

It wasn't until the concert ended that I found out what had happened. The office staff had planned a party after the show ended and had brought with them a large supply of liquor. The first mistake they had made was not to invite the orchestra members from the plant. Their second mistake was to leave the booze in the waiting-room near the stage. Now, these amateur musicians were no amateurs at the drinking game; they knew about the party and that they hadn't been invited. They had drunk the entire supply of liquor while the rest of the program was being presented.

In 1938, Mary and I first heard a poem, "The Cause," that had been written thirty-five years earlier by an American clergyman, Edward Cantrell. Composed as a personal creed, it only came to light in 1935 when Louis Adamic included it in a book called *My America*. The poem had a profound effect on both of us, and Mary's first Christmas gift to me after our marriage was *My America*. It contributed significantly to my development of the caring community model (in contrast to the traditional medical model) as the optimal milieu for the successful treatment of addiction. It begins as follows:

If you accept life, and are willing to exalt it
above names, phrases, and things;
If you accept truth, and after the severest tests,
are not afraid;
If you accept brotherliness as better than the
hates of the jungle;
If you love justice, and hate the very semblance
of exploitation;
If you love work as the expression of the Creative
Idea,
Then let us work together; we will be comrades!

At work, things were going fairly smoothly for me. One fine spring morning in 1939 I went up to the top of one of the reducers and out onto the roof. It was still early, just as the sun was coming up, and I was thinking about how everything was going so well — my marriage, my work at the plant, and my plans to return to university in the fall. I looked south, and in the distance saw Lake Erie, just as the rays of the sun were beginning to glint off the water. It was very still, quiet, peaceful. Then suddenly I had a unique experience that I can only describe as transcendental. In the midst of this tranquility, I lost my fear of not being able to succeed, and I acquired a new sense of direction in personal fulfilment. From then on my anxiety in times of crisis was markedly diminished.

A month later I went to Toronto for an interview with Dr. Stanley Ryerson, the assistant dean of medicine at the University of Toronto, concerning my application to re-enrol. The interview did not go well. Dr. Ryerson had studied my academic record between 1930 and 1935, and had decided before meeting me that he would not agree to my return to medical school. He was polite, but firm.

He repeatedly stated that he did not feel I was suited for a medical career, given my low grades in the previous years. But I too was stubborn. I knew with utter certainty that this was something I really had to do, and I would not budge. He dismissed me several times, but I refused to leave the room.

After a while I could see that he was getting desperate, wondering what to do. Would he call the university police? Finally, in exasperation, he said, "Can you not appreciate that you have neither the intelligence nor the emotional stability to graduate in medicine and succeed as a physician?"

I said no, I could not, and still refused to leave. Finally he said to me, "Look, I want you to see Dr. William Blatz, a professor of psychology at our university, and I am quite certain that he will agree with me." Fortunately he was able to arrange for an interview with Dr. Blatz immediately. This resulted in a second, equally memorable meeting for me that day, with one of the outstanding psychologists of the time.

Dr. William Blatz was particularly famous for his pioneering work with children — their problems, their management, and their educational needs. I answered in detail all the questions he asked about my life up to that point. When the interview ended, he said, "I cannot agree with Dr. Ryerson, and I shall see what I can do." As I left I heard him ask his secretary to get Dr. Ryerson on the phone. Only as a result of Dr. Blatz's intervention was I accepted into medical school, but I was so angry with Dr. Ryerson that I swore to myself, "I'll show him if it's the last thing I do!" When I returned to university that fall I was determined to succeed, and it showed in my improved study habits.

That summer slowly drew to an end and I spent my final days at the Inco plant, which turned out to be a very moving experience. One after another, my co-workers came up to say good-bye and to wish me good luck. Some of them suggested that I would forget all about them once I went back to the big university, but I assured them I wouldn't, and I never have. Joe La Capria was particularly interested in, and concerned about, my future. He repeatedly asked if we had enough money. "I have saved some money," he said. "If you need money, you come to see me." I didn't realize then that because of the demands of university life and military service, I would never see him again.

Our plans to move to Toronto were somewhat complicated by the fact that Mary was now pregnant, and we would have to be very careful with our finances. Upon my formal acceptance into third-year medicine, I returned to Toronto and found an apartment for us at 230 Spadina Road, just below Casa Loma, the famous castle built by Sir Henry Pellatt in 1914. To help with the finances, Mary's brother, who was already living in Toronto and working for a brokerage firm, moved in with us as a boarder. Joe Lamping was soon to join the Army Dental Corps, later graduate in dentistry, and spend his life in that profession.

One of the problems I faced returning to school for the third-year medical course was that the anatomy of the body below the neck course was part of the second-year curriculum. At the end of the third year, which covered the head and neck, the examination tested the student's knowledge of the entire body, not just what had been covered that year. It had been four years since I had studied second-year anatomy, and I had not done so very successfully even then. I was fully aware of the difficulties I would face in trying to catch up.

Soon after starting back, I saw a notice on a bulletin board in the medical school advertising a skeleton for sale. An elderly physician in the west end of the city was selling the skeleton because he was retiring from practice. I immediately went to see him and found the skeleton in perfect condition, actually better than those at the medical school, which had been handled by so many students.

And it cost only thirty dollars. Somehow I managed to transport my new friend on the public-transit system to our apartment on Spadina Road. I named him George, and propped him up in an armchair in the living-room when I was not studying anatomy. Mary, Joe, and I soon came to regard him as just another member of the family. Eventually we became so accustomed to having him around that one day Mary forgot to advise the new cleaning-lady that he presided over the living-room. The first time she walked into the room she shrieked so loudly she could have wakened the dead.

At school and at home, I set myself a rigorous study timetable, and worked from 7:00 P.M. to 11:00 P.M. or midnight every night of the week from the time I started back to school. Since Mary was pregnant, she made no attempt to find a job during the fall of 1939, and our baby, Bobby, was born on January 26, 1940. When I learned in May that I had received As in all my subjects — except bacteriology, for which I had received a B — and that I had placed seventh in a class of ninety-seven, I knew that this time I would succeed in medical school.

After receiving the good news of my accomplishments I was approached by one of my professors, who suggested that I should seriously consider trying the examinations for the primary fellowship in the Royal College of Physicians and Surgeons of Canada. If one aspired to become a fellow of the Royal College in those days, it was important to have advanced knowledge of the normal body. If I wanted to take the examinations, I would have to study all summer, which meant not being able to work to add to my funds for tuition. Mary and I discussed the situation, and I decided to do it. I spent the entire summer back at the university reviewing the work in anatomy, physiology, biochemistry, and histology that I had been studying during the year. Once again, old George came in handy.

Examinations for the primary fellowship were held in two parts — a written examination in September and an oral test at McGill University in Montreal scheduled for the end of October. I was well prepared, and all seemed to be going well. In fact, I had just received word that I had passed the written part of the examination, and I can vividly remember one warm September evening walking with Mary near our new home on Millwood Road. I recall remarking how well everything was turning out. Life was almost too good to be true. A few days later, disaster struck.

On October 4, 1940, I was working in a chemistry laboratory at the Banting Institute with my lab partner, Staph Barootes (later Senator Barootes), when I was summoned to the telephone. It was Mary, calling to tell me that she had been called at the office where she had been working and notified that our eight-month-old son, Bobby, had died in his carriage during his afternoon nap. Our pediatrician called it a crib death.

We were shattered. Somehow I managed to hold myself together long enough to go to McGill and try the oral examinations. Later that same day, I learned that I had been among those who had passed. My fellowship was little consolation. That evening, the reality of Bobby's death finally caught up to me, and for the next two months I was severely depressed and had great difficulty in concentrating on my studies. Mary was equally devastated, so we were not much help to each other during those dreadful weeks. Finally I realized that I had to talk with somebody, and I thought of one of my father's distant cousins, Alice Thompson, whom I had known and admired since childhood days. At that time she was the chief public-health nurse for the city of Toronto, and I felt I could talk to her. We met at her comfortable home on Castlefield Avenue, and we must have talked for three or four hours. The conversation represented a turning point for me. Alice did almost all the listening while I unburdened myself of my depression, anger, and frustration. My release from these crippling, suppressed emotions freed me to better support Mary in her grief and to reapply myself to my studies. By June I stood seventh in our class of 108. Fourth-year medicine was now behind me.

I did not know it then, but the summer I had spent studying for the fellowship eventually had a permanent and significant impact on my professional career and objectives. More advanced study of the human body and its functions meant that anatomy, physiology, and biochemistry were no longer individual subjects I had to pass in order to proceed with the medical courses. At this level, I found my knowledge coming together and I could begin to visualize the function and potential of the body as a whole — its intricacy, integration, and wondrous adaptability. Long before I graduated I had become much more interested in the normal, healthy body and the promotion of health, rather than the abnormal body and treatment of disease. At that time, however, I had yet to discover how this interest could make it possible for me to make a living for myself and my family. In the early 1940s, preventive medicine and the concept of total health were a long way off.

As it happened, I did not have to spend the summer of 1941 studying, and I was fortunate to find work in the shipping department of Canada Bud Brewery, which was located in Toronto on the north side of Dundas Street, between University Avenue and McCaul Street. This job enabled me to learn something about the brewery business from the inside — the strict regulations about cleanliness, the employees' pride in their product, and most importantly for my later use, to witness how the pros, with their ready access to beer, could drink moderate quantities that avoided trouble for themselves and others. Excessive or uncontrolled drinking by employees was not tolerated. I never thought that a few years later I would be trying to treat those for whom the excessive consumption of alcohol had become a serious health problem.

Early in fifth-year medicine I was appointed president of our class, and soon after the annual medical banquet was held in Hart House. The head table consisted of most of the medical faculty, including Dean Gallie, Assistant Dean Ryerson (my old nemesis), and Canon Cody, president of the university. A certain number of the students remained true to medical-student tradition on this occasion and managed to drink too much, but the situation got out of hand when one of them threw a bun that hit President Cody on the head. The shocked reaction of those at the head table and the other students effectively dampened the festivities after that, and the evening wound down rather unpleasantly. The following day President Cody summoned the dean and some of the faculty members and gave them a very severe dressing-down for their inability to control the students. The dean and his colleagues were in a very sour mood when they returned to the medical building. We were fortunate that Professor Wastenys, our professor of biochemistry, who was recognized among us as the student's best friend, tipped us off that those found responsible would be severely punished.

"Unless you act quickly," the professor said, "and impose your own punishment on those responsible for the incidents at the banquet, one or more of you are liable to be expelled." The executive of the Student Medical Society, of which I was a member, quickly held an emergency meeting, and we agreed to levy a stiff fine on those responsible and a smaller fine for the accomplices. When we were called before the dean we were able to report what we had done, and he agreed not to impose further punishment. This was my baptism into involvement and responsibility for student affairs.

A significant number of students in my year were Jewish and I became concerned about the fact that they always sat together at one side of the lecture room. I found this division unacceptable and I went to Murray Acker, now a prominent psychiatrist in private practice in Toronto, to suggest that we should do something about the situation. Murray had no official position in our class but was well regarded by all the students. I suggested to Murray that he work with the Jewish students and I would work with the others to discontinue this extension of prejudice and to do what we could to facilitate friendlier relationships among all the students. Long before the year ended, the breakdown of students into Jewish and non-Jewish groups had disappeared.

In the meantime, an equally serious problem was developing, and it took up a considerable amount of time of the executive of the Medical Society. Canada was at war, and the Department of National Defence urgently needed more physicians. It had instructed all the medical schools in Canada to speed up the curriculum and graduate new physicians as quickly as possible. This meant that our four-month summer vacation was to be taken away from us, even though these months were the only time in which many students could earn enough money to pay their tuition. There were many suggestions made concerning extra bursaries, loans, and other options that both faculty members and executives of the Medical Society considered. Similar discussions went on at other medical schools across Canada. The students themselves finally came up with a suggestion that was accepted by both the federal government and the universities. We were to be allowed to enlist in the army as privates, be paid a private's salary of $1.30 a day, and given leave of absence for our medical studies until we had graduated.

Our class finished fifth year early in 1942, and we immediately entered our sixth and final year. Shortly thereafter, we were allowed to enlist as privates in the Royal Canadian Army Medical Corps. It was about this time that I was elected president of the Medical Society. The presidents of the various student societies, such as arts, engineering, dentistry, and medicine, formed the Students' Administrative Council of the university. The members of this council then elected a vice-president from among their members, and I was so honored in the spring of 1942. The president of the council was always a university graduate. However in 1942 all potential candidates for the position were in military service, so I became acting president until my graduation in January 1943, when I was elected president, a position I held during my eight-month internship at St. Michael's Hospital in Toronto. So, in addition to trying to graduate in medicine that year, I was both president of the Medical Society and acting president of the Students' Administrative Council. Although the extra responsibilities in my final year increased the day-to-day stress and significantly reduced my time for study, I welcomed the opportunity to test my ability to cope with additional pressures.

In September 1942, Eleanor Roosevelt sponsored an international student assembly in Washington, D.C., to encourage a joint effort toward peace and provide a forum for an exchange of ideas by the future leaders of our generation. It brought together several hundred delegates from all the countries at war with the Axis powers. The Canadian delegation consisted of students from all the Canadian universities. As the head of the Students' Administrative Council for the largest of these delegations, I was chosen as speaker and leader of the Canadian delegation. I persuaded the group that I should also bring Mary along, since an occasion of such importance required the presence of a secretary.

It was a proud day for the Canadian delegation when we were invited to have breakfast with Eleanor Roosevelt in the White House. We all sat at a long table, with the First Lady at the head. I was on her right, Mary on her left, and the delegation had a wonderful opportunity to talk with this truly remarkable lady. While we were there, President Roosevelt delivered one of his famous fireside radio chats to the nation. On this particular occasion the leaders of the student delegations were invited to be present in the Oval Office while the President delivered his message. For those of us present, this was the highlight of the trip. After an aide cautioned us to be quiet during the chat, Roosevelt looked up with his famous grin and long cigarette holder and added, "And don't sneeze."

There was one surprise left for me, and it came on the day the closing ceremonies were to take place in the Department of Labor auditorium. An hour or so before the ceremonies were to begin, the head of the American student body came to me and said, "We want you to be co-chairman, on behalf of all the students, with Chief Justice Robert Jackson" (who was later to become world-famous for his work at the Nuremberg trials). It was quite an event. The flags of all the nations represented were on the stage; the U.S. Marine Band was in the orchestra pit. It was my responsibility to call up the leader of each national student group to stand by his or her appropriate flag while the band played the national anthem for that country. My only script for this effort was a hand-written piece of foolscap with the countries listed in alphabetical order. It had been quite noticeable during the conference that there was considerable jockeying for prominence between the U.S.A. and the U.S.S.R. delegations and there had apparently been much discussion as to which of the two should be called first to the platform. Both "U.S." and "U.S.S.R." had been scratched out and rewritten on my sheet so often that when I came to the U.S.'s turn I missed it entirely! The American flag stood alone while I completed the rest of the list. Eventually I realized why I was being signalled so frantically from the audience, and I called up the chief American delegate with the words, "Finally, the representative of our host nation, the United States of America." The American chap came up onto the platform and stood by his flag while the band struck up "The Star-Spangled Banner." Chief Justice William O. Douglas delivered the closing address, which brought to an end one of the most memorable — and potentially embarrassing — times of my life.

There was one major development in my final year at medical school which helped to determine my postgraduate activities immediately thereafter and eventually my life's work. Mary and I were just getting by financially, and could certainly have made use of extra money. I had learned that the Toronto Psychiatric Hospital was looking for three senior medical students to take blood and urine samples from new patients each morning, and to do the lab work on the specimens after school each day. I applied for one of the positions and was hired. We were not paid in cash, but we got all our meals there for nothing, which was a significant consideration. Also, during the two weeks' vacation we were allowed during the war (instead of our normal four months) we worked full-time at the hospital and were actually assigned some work with the patients.

It was here that I met Dr. George Scott. He was interested in my extracurricular activities with the Students' Administrative Council, my trip to Washington, and my initial attempts at therapy with selected psychiatric patients during my two-week vacation. My relationship with him became an important factor in my work while I was in the army, which in turn led to my activities after my discharge from the armed forces.

On January 27, 1943, at long last I received my medical degree. I was also very pleased at that time to be one of four students in my year to receive the honor award of the Students' Administrative Council for my contribution to the undergraduate life of the university. Following my graduation I was posted to St. Michael's Hospital in Toronto for the eight-month general internship that the army allowed medical students before they were posted to active duty. In those days the junior interns had extra responsibilities, because several of the staff physicians were away on military service. As a result, many of us relied on the experience of the head nurses at an early stage, and I was particularly indebted to Grace Murphy, the highly respected head nurse on the medical service where I was first assigned.

About a month after I began my internship, a young woman in her early twenties was admitted and diagnosed as having pneumococcal meningitis. Neurologist Dr.

Edward Brooks was the staff physician responsible for her. When we discussed her case he confided to me that they had never had a recovery from pneumococcal meningitis in that hospital. However, he felt there was an outside chance that she could survive with continuous intravenous medication of one of the sulfa drugs, soludagenan. Sulfonamides had first been used in 1936 to treat a variety of medical conditions, and they were considered a potential panacea when they first appeared on the market (much as penicillin was perceived to be a miracle drug when it was introduced later that same year). Dr. Brooks also pointed out to me that it was very important to ensure that the drug did not clog the ureters which connect the kidneys to the bladder. Such a complication could cause death from uremia. He said that this could best be avoided with the continuous intravenous administration of saline.

I was assigned to the patient. Grace Murphy worked with me closely and made sure that the other nurses had instructions to call me at the first indication that the treatment was not working properly. Our patient became the first one at St. Michael's Hospital to recover from the disease. Dr. Brooks was so pleased that he insisted we write an article together about the case, which duly appeared in the April 1943 issue of the *Ontario Medical Review*.

We junior interns had many other opportunities to assume responsibilities that we normally would have waited much longer to tackle. Dr. James Danis was a member of the surgical staff who specialized in bowel surgery, including hemorrhoids. Like other staff doctors he was overworked, and had limited time to give detailed instructions to the younger interns. I once assisted him, along with Eric Grundy, another student from my year, at a hemorrhoid operation. The next day, as the number of waiting patients grew, Dr. Danis told the two of us, "You take over that next patient from the public ward." Eric and I stared at each other in amazement, wondering what to do. We finally decided that I would operate on one side, with him as assistant, and then he would be the surgeon on the other side, with me as assistant.

Once we got going, we got caught up in the challenge and decided to do the best job possible. We snipped off everything that wasn't flush with the surface tissue, and carefully put in stitches where they were required. When we had finished we figured we had done fairly neat work. Neither of us, however, slept well that night, wondering whether the patient might hemmorhage, or what we would do if any serious complications arose. But the man had an uneventful recovery, and we both began to give serious consideration to pursuing surgery as a specialty. We soon got over the urge.

Another unique experience for us that year was the chance to work in the emergency department. Since St. Mike's is situated in the heart of downtown Toronto, emergency patients arrived at all hours of the night. Scalp wounds and other lacerations from fights and a host of other minor injuries were quite common, as was a wide variety of more serious conditions requiring immediate attention and admission. Once again the junior interns were often on their own for two or three hours at a time, although senior staff members were always on call. We practised sewing up scalp lacerations and attended to many other injuries independently. When we left the eight-month internship program, we were already veterans of a sort.

Since we were permitted only those eight months of internship, I left St. Michael's in September 1943, at which time those of us in my year were promoted to first lieutenant and sent to Camp Borden for some basic military training. My most vivid memories of the camp are of sore feet and muscles. Fortunately I was soon promoted to captain. I was one of a handful of my classmates who were assigned to a six-month crash course in psychiatry at Christie Street Hospital (the Veterans' Hospital in Toronto prior to the founding of Sunnybrook), Toronto General

Hospital, and the Toronto Psychiatric Hospital. I reported to Christie Street Hospital in mid-December 1943, and came under the direction of Dr. William Bailey.

I was not at the hospital very long before a lieutenant in the navy was admitted and diagnosed as having pneumococcal meningitis. I sat in on the medical meeting while the case of Charles Meredith was discussed. Dr. Bailey predicted that the patient would be dead by Christmas Day; the head of surgery said that he would be dead sooner than that. I went to Dr. Bailey and asked if I could have complete control of the patient's case. He listened to my account of the St. Michael's Hospital case and immediately consented. I arranged to move into the hospital so that I could be close to the patient at all times. I also arranged to have blood and urine tests taken every six hours and a spinal-fluid analysis every twelve. At that time penicillin was just beginning to be used, but it was in very short supply. The physician in charge of its distribution locally was Dr. Ray Farquharson, my former professor of medicine, then a senior medical officer in the RCAF. I contacted him, explained my situation, and requested approval to add penicillin to the soludagenan treatment I had used at St. Michael's. Dr. Farquharson agreed, the penicillin was made available, and treatment on Charles Meredith began immediately.

During his treatment I did spinal taps at noon and midnight, kept the intravenous going steadily, repeated the Soludagenan treatment used at St. Michael's, and added the penicillin. The lab was kept busy analyzing all the blood and urine specimens we were sending down. To my delight and that of the patient's young bride, my patient made a complete recovery. Dr. Farquharson had me write up the case and present it at a meeting of local physicians in military service.

As a postscript to this story, I was the luncheon speaker at a Kiwanis Club meeting in the Royal York Hotel in Toronto forty-two years later. Sitting close to the head table was a married couple, both smiling broadly and waving to me as I sat down. Learning that I would be speaking that day, Charles Meredith and his wife had arranged to attend the meeting. After my talk, my former patient stood up and explained to the group how I had helped to save his life in 1943. I found the moment very touching, one of my happiest memories of the exciting days before I eventually stumbled into the addiction-treatment field.

CHAPTER FOUR

Army Days

By 1944, senior staff of the Canadian armed forces were becoming alarmed at the number of new recruits being rejected on grounds of instability, and about the number of men who had broken down emotionally on active duty and were subsequently discharged. The situation had become acute by the time Canadian forces were involved in the battle for Italy. Accordingly, the army established five conditioning centers across Canada — at Gordon Head, British Columbia; Portage La Prairie, Manitoba; Brampton, Ontario; Huntingdon, Quebec; and Sussex, New Brunswick. These were set up to expedite soldiers' recovery from war wounds, surgery, and other disabilities. Their programs were a combination of military and therapeutic exercises, under the supervision of officers skilled in both disciplines. It was decided that a new wing would also be added to the conditioning centers, and those in charge of them would be responsible for psychological retraining of the men who were potential candidates for dismissal, either because of their states of anxiety or depression during active duty or while on basic- or advanced-training programs in Canada.

The officer in charge of psychiatric services for the Canadian Army was Colonel Jack Griffin, and it became his responsibility to see that these centers were established as quickly as possible. The situation led to some ingenious ad-lib planning. The person responsible for designing the program to be used in the new wings was Major George Scott, the psychiatrist I had met during my final year at medical school. Dr. Scott had been told to move swiftly with the new program, and he began by setting up an exploratory training center at North Bay, Ontario. When I completed my postgraduate training in psychiatry in the spring of 1944, I was summoned to North Bay to work with Dr. Scott. Under his supervision I was introduced to some of the ideas he had developed for the programs in the new wings of the centers. I was in North Bay for about three weeks, and then was abruptly transferred to No. 2 Conditioning Centre in Brampton.

The pressure to get these psychological wings (thereafter known as "D" wings) established quickly was so great that there had not been time to have the units officially recognized with a budget for staff and equipment. On paper, I was listed as being on staff at No. 2 Depot in Toronto and my equipment in Brampton consisted initially of one empty H-hut. Of course, this did not stop the first patients from pouring in from Camp Borden and other bases in Ontario, and I found myself desperately short of staff. So when they checked in and started to tell me their troubles, I interrupted them and said, "Don't tell me your troubles. *I'm* the one who's in trouble. What can you do to help me out?" As a result I trained some of the first people to take case histories of other patients and assigned others to administrative responsibilities. The fact that they arrived with their own medical records was a big help to me in quickly selecting the right people for the right jobs.

One of my first patients was a sergeant whom I immediately put in charge of daily schedules. I told him to make sure that the men went to bed at the right time, got up when they were supposed to, attended meals, and so on. But he had to be careful about how he carried out his task. The guidelines from Dr. Scott were very general with regard to things like discipline: "Just reintroduce them to the army more gently than the first time around, and help restore their confidence in themselves so that they can be upgraded to play useful roles in military service." In hindsight, the whole situation was very unusual. Whenever I encountered a serious new problem and phoned Major Scott for advice, his reaction was usually one of amusement at my predicament. The more trouble I got into and the more concerned I became, the more he chuckled. I quickly came to understand what he had expected of me when he told me to be innovative.

One of the techniques he had suggested in the guidelines developed at North Bay was to explore the possible effectiveness of music therapy. I decided it was worth a try, but since we had no budget or musical instruments I could not see how we could begin. I went to Dr. Charles Peaker for advice. He was a well-known organist and choirmaster at St. Paul's Anglican Church in Toronto. We discussed the possibility of taking the patients as one group, getting them to sing together as well as they could, then dividing their number in half, quarters, eighths, and so on until eventually they would end up singing solos. We thought we might slowly improve their capacity for joint effort, as well as increase their confidence in their own abilities. When I pointed out to Dr. Peaker that we had no music instructor, and that I was personally unequal to the task, he amazed me by volunteering to come out himself to help get the program started. He would not charge for his efforts, asking only that we somehow provide him with a piano. I wasn't sure how to get one, but I did not want to lose a wonderful opportunity.

By this time the other convalescents at No. 2 Conditioning Centre had begun calling our D wing the "Ding-Wing." One of my patients was a corporal who was a most interesting and talented person. Corporal McDonald was from Cape Breton, Nova Scotia, and his military record indicated a touch of psychopathic behavior. He was always very sharply dressed, had the right answer to every question and situation, and generally gave a favorable impression of himself.

One morning not long after I had my meeting with Dr. Peaker, I summoned the corporal and said, "McDonald, I want you to take the day off, hitchhike to Toronto, and see if you can possibly find anyone who will loan or give us a piano so that we can begin adding music therapy to this program."

"Yes, sir," he said, and took off immediately. He returned that evening, saluted smartly, and said, "The piano will arrive tomorrow, sir." When I asked him where the piano was coming from, he replied, "There is a lady in the west end of Toronto who is so heartbroken over the plight of us emotionally disturbed recruits that she is donating her piano and paying for its delivery herself." Sure enough, the piano arrived the next day and we were able to get our music-therapy program off the ground.

I had similar success with Corporal McDonald when I needed some office equipment. One day a very shaky little private arrived on our wing. When I asked him what he did, he said that he was a typist. When he started to tell me his problems, I said, "We'll get around to your problems later. Your job is in that office looking after our records, right away." The trouble was, we had no typewriter, so I called in McDonald again and said to him, "Corporal, I want you to take the day off, hitchhike to Toronto, and see if you can get us a typewriter this time."

"Yes, sir," he said smartly, and was off again. That afternoon he returned with a new little portable machine.

"How did you manage to get it?" I asked.

"Sir," he replied, "don't ask too many questions about this typewriter." So I didn't.

In the meantime, Major Scott found me an excellent training officer, Lieutenant Bill Newman. He had been overseas with the tank corps in Italy and had been sent back to Canada to recover from an emotional breakdown during active duty. Bill was a very valuable addition to our staff, and the place began to shape up much better after his arrival. Another new patient was a staff-sergeant who had just returned from a stint in England. He was a precision drillmaster, just the sort of person we needed, since my gang did not yet look very impressive on the parade square compared to the others in the center. I called the new staff-sergeant aside and said, "Your job is to make this crowd into a precision drill squad." He undertook the assignment with vigor, and before long my patients began to look very smart indeed on parade.

At this point, one of my first patients came up to me and said, "Sir, we would like to have a serious chat with you. You have us looking pretty sharp on the parade ground, but wherever did you get that battledress?" I was impressed by his direct approach.

"Well," I replied, "it's issue, like everybody else's."

"I've had a chat with a fellow sergeant, the base tailor, and we've arranged for him to measure you so that you can have your uniform altered. You have to be the sharpest-looking officer if we're going to be the sharpest-looking squad."

So I was ushered over to the tailor and turned out as sharply as he and my discerning critics desired. I was also very pleased with the results, and I took my group's interest in my appearance as a healthy sign.

I continued to put many of the patients in charge of various duties. And there was lots of work for them to do, including some "home" improvements. For example, one side of our H-hut was our living quarters, and the other side was for administration, lectures, group discussion, and other therapies. However, we needed a partition to separate one half of the H-hut into two parts. As usual, the problem was how to get the material to build it. Fortunately I had become quite adept at getting things done, by means that were not always according to army regulations.

During all of these activities I was under the direction of Major Stanley Montgomery, the senior officer at No. 2 Conditioning Centre. Major Montgomery was a stickler for army etiquette and procedures, and he took a very dim view of my methods of procuring both equipment and staff. I had repeatedly asked him (with no success) for enough lumber to make the partition, because at that time there was still no official approval of a budget for our Ding-Wing.

The camp at Brampton had been under canvas with wooden floors when the war began in 1939. It was subsequently replaced by buildings, although sections of the floorboards that had been under the tents were still piled in an adjacent field. I inspected it and found the wood in good condition. The problem was how to use it quickly. I did not want to ask Major Montgomery for it because I was certain he would turn me down, at least until he had received permission from his superiors that its use for a partition in D wing was proper. I did not want to wait that long for something I considered so essential.

By this time I had upwards of forty men under my care, and one of them was a private who was a carpenter in civilian life. I had a confidential chat with him and asked if he could supervise turning the lumber into a partition with a door if I could figure out some way to get it. He assured me that it would not be a problem, and I pondered how to get hold of the material. Luckily, Major Montgomery decided at about the same time to take the whole No. 2 Conditioning Centre on a route march. I excused my group from the march, saying that our program for that day was already planned, and he agreed that we could stay behind.

I called my men together and told them about the march: "As soon as the rest of the camp is out of sight, you are to come under the direction of this private (the carpenter), including the officers and NCOs. He is the foreman in charge of getting that lumber over here, and we'll build the partition, which has to be finished before they get back." There were no complaints, and the whole gang had a great afternoon. They all knew perfectly well that I was not supposed to be doing this, and they worked with a will.

With the collusion of the quartermaster, who was also a major, I had managed to get the nails, hammers, and saws necessary to build the partition. He had maintained a tolerant and amused attitude to all our activities in the Ding-Wing.

The partition was completed in good time. When Major Montgomery eventually stomped into our hut, he was so angry I thought he was going to explode. I tried to play dumb and said that I didn't realize that the material could not be used for our partition. I also played up the fact that I had not been in the army very long and was, therefore, not familiar with all the regulations. I had expected a hostile reaction, but had gambled that at least he would not order us to take down the partition. To our delight, the partition remained intact, and the quartermaster was greatly diverted by watching Major Montgomery dress me down.

Now that our separate lecture room was in place, I turned my attention to the bare walls, and decided that a bit of interior decorating would further improve the morale of my patients. To introduce the men gently back into army life, I decided to incorporate some of the features they had known in their civilian lives into our setting. Why not some art on the walls? I had become acquainted with Blair Laing of Laing Art Galleries in Toronto during my first attempt at university in the early 1930s. I asked him if he would agree to hang some of his pictures around the Brampton lecture room and then replace them monthly with others for variety, and he agreed. As a result, our lecture room was soon decorated with art better than in many an officers' mess.

Our "fine-arts" program helped to enhance the image of the whole place. Dr. Peaker was coming out to our conditioning center once a week to teach music, and his visits were quite successful. I was giving some of the lectures, as was Lieutenant Newman. The precision drill was also progressing well, and the men were looking very sharp on parade. By the fall of 1944, I had begun to think that we had significantly improved the morale and emotional stability of most of our patients. Much of the credit had to go to Dorothy Madgett, a physiotherapist who had been at No. 2 Conditioning Centre when it opened and held the rank of first lieutenant. She was particularly skilled in the art of progressive relaxation, and her instruction in those techniques became an integral part of our entire rehabilitation program.

In October 1944, Brigadier Reese, the chief psychiatrist for the British armed forces, visited Canada. Colonel Jack Griffin arranged for the brigadier to inspect our work at the psychological retraining center in Brampton, and he and his escort arrived on a cold, windy afternoon. We had learned that the visit would be a short one, which meant that there would not be sufficient time for him to examine our entire operation in detail. I told our precision-drill sergeant to take the men out on the parade ground and demonstrate to our visitors just what they could do. They all looked good from a distance, and there was no way that an outsider could tell that some of them were still in a very shaky state.

We received a subsequent visit from two psychiatrists from the No. 2 Depot in Toronto, who assessed our patients at the completion of their psychological retraining program. About one-third of those who had finished the program were graded as unsuitable for military service and these men were recommended for discharge. Another third were evaluated as suitable for continuing service within Canada, and the final third were considered capable of overseas duty. In view of our ad-lib approach to treatment, I found these results quite encouraging.

In late April 1945, I was transferred to No. 5 Conditioning Centre in Sussex, New Brunswick. Mary and I were not pleased with this move because she was expecting another child at any moment. The move to New Brunswick presented me with the challenge of a new clinical situation. Since the war in Europe was almost over, my immediate task was now to prepare emotionally disabled veterans for their return to civilian life, rather than for their eventual return to the armed forces. Accordingly, the service was referred to as a "psychological rehabilitation center" rather than a "psychological retraining center." Our patients would be returning to their homes in the Maritime provinces, and following periods of front-line duty, their most common disability was severe chronic anxiety.

By this time the psychological wings of the conditioning centers had acquired official recognition and budgets, so we were able to put together proper staff, which now included a physician, a psychologist, nurses, and other support personnel. My responsibilities were also more varied than they had been at Brampton, since I was also on the staff of the Sussex Military Hospital, which was located on the same base. I was expected to attend the rounds at the hospital as often as possible, and I welcomed the opportunity to reacquaint myself with some of the basic medical situations comparable to those I had encountered at St. Michael's Hospital.

It was in the course of one of my medical rounds that I was present during a detailed discussion regarding a patient with hyperthyroidism. The doctors were all standing around his bed as his case was being debated with the other medical staff. The young private certainly exhibited all the major signs and symptoms of the disease, including an elevated basal metabolic rate. During the consultation, I noticed something about his eyes that puzzled me. He appeared unusually bright and alert for someone sick enough to be confined to bed. When we had completed our rounds, I asked the major in charge if the hyperthyroid patient might be well enough to come down to my office for an interview. The major approved, although this did not sit well with the nurses, who seemed unhappy to have one of their favorite patients pulled out of bed.

The private arrived at my office bundled up in his dressing-gown. I asked him to sit down and repeat for me the history of his condition right from the start. He did so, and provided a detailed description that made me even more suspicious. How could anyone without any kind of medical or nursing training know so much about hyperthyroidism? Finally I said, "Bill, how long have you been getting away with this story?"

Without the slightest hesitation he replied, "I've been doing okay up to now."

"You get back to your ward, get dressed, and come back and see me right away," I said.

When he returned I took him over to see the colonel in charge of the hospital. It was apparent that my superior was having difficulty being both stern and amused at the same time. I told him that I needed a secretary and a personal assistant to run errands, and I thought that this young man would be perfect for the job. The colonel readily agreed, so for the rest of my term at Sussex and for a short time thereafter, Bill became my secretary, general assistant, and jack-of-all-trades. The fact that I had seen through his charade seemed to have elevated me in his estimation, and during the time he worked for me I had no trouble with him.

At Sussex I learned of a new treatment from Major Scott. He had outlined for me the techniques of administering small doses of standard insulin to help facilitate some patients' recovery from states of severe anxiety. In fact, during the latter years of my army service it became the vogue to treat severe anxiety states like this in doses carefully calculated to induce sweating and relaxation but without pushing the patient into insulin shock. The usual dose per patient was ten to twenty units of standard insulin, depending on various factors, including the patient's body weight.

This treatment was carried out in our H-hut, one half of which was now the sleeping quarters and the other the mess hall with the dining-room and the kitchen. The insulin was administered first thing in the morning in the sleeping quarters while all the officers and staff watched the patient's reaction to the drug. Major Scott had instructed me to allow a patient's reaction to continue for two hours, unless the latter reacted badly. In that case we had orange juice available for the patient to drink in order to interrupt or reduce the reaction. We had trained the entire staff in the signs and symptoms of the more serious levels of the insulin effect.

I was impressed with the effectiveness of the treatment. Extreme anxiety produced increased heart rate and blood pressure, severe insomnia and tremor, impaired appetite, and impotence. This last disability seemed to worry most of the men more than anything else, until we explained to them that it was part of the general syndrome of acute sustained anxiety and would disappear once their emotional states improved.

After the two-hour treatment period the patients all had ravenous appetites. The insulin reaction was halted by breakfast, served in bed by the clinical staff and officers. The patients thoroughly enjoyed this attention, and often snapped their fingers at their "waiters," calling for faster service or for second helpings. The insulin seemed to break the general pattern of acute anxiety, and when their appetites returned the patients were less anxious, calmer, and better able to sleep soundly. Little did I know how important this experience would be later when I sought more effective means of interrupting states of alcohol intoxication.

To further reintroduce our patients to civilian life, we arranged for a bus to take us all to the seashore for a picnic. All ranks, patients and staff alike, co-operated in the preparations for the event, and we obtained some beer from the wet canteen, the sergeants' mess, and the officers' mess. I made it my responsibility to ensure that the quantity of alcoholic beverages would not be sufficient to cause any trouble for the staff or anyone else at the picnic.

The picnic was one of our last festive occasions together. Soon afterwards, the dismantling of the entire operation at No. 5 Conditioning Centre began, including our psychological rehabilitation center. At the time there was no comparable service anywhere in the Maritimes, so I tried (unsuccessfully) to explore some ways of continuing the center under new management. Our staff had come from various parts of Canada, however, and they wanted to return to their homes. There was no new agency prepared to take over, not even the Department of Veterans Affairs. I was distressed to learn that the remaining serious cases would be transferred to various provincial mental hospitals, but there was nothing I could do about it. In November 1945, I myself was transferred back to No. 2 Depot in Toronto. I was later posted to the Toronto Psychiatric Hospital until the spring of 1946, when I was discharged from the army.

A civilian once again, I was now faced with the dilemma of what to do with my medical and related training. I also had to worry about how to take care of a wife and two children — Ronnie, who was born in October 1943, and Janice, who arrived in May 1945. Up to that point I had received comparable training in both medicine and psychiatry, but not enough to qualify as a specialist in either. I had enjoyed the unique chance to organize a mental-health service in a new, untried situation and had worked with a multidisciplinary team involved in both treatment and leisure activities with the patients. But how could I make use of this expertise?

Mary suggested that I open up a general practice, but I knew that I was insufficiently trained in many areas of medicine, such as obstetrics, to be an effective family practitioner. I also knew that I would quickly become bored operating a full-time general practice. I believed that my skills in the medical field could best be put to use by establishing clinics to treat people with emotional disorders. I could not see many other alternatives; I certainly could not afford to return to medical school to hone other medical skills.

After discussing my future plans with various experts in the health-care field, I decided to set up a clinic for the emotionally disabled, comparable to the ones I had developed in the army. I then went to Dr. Clare Buck, who was then the deputy minister of health for Ontario. He agreed with my plan, but recommended that I should begin on a small scale by taking advantage of an old statute that allowed any physician in the province to take up to four patients for treatment into his own home. Mary had always had a sense of adventure and she courageously agreed to this plan after I reassured her that the worst we could expect would be three or four nervous old ladies as guests. I had no idea at the time that our only patients would be alcoholics.

CHAPTER FIVE

Glenmaple

Our adventure began with the search for a place to live and in which to treat our patients. After looking far and wide we found a home about fifteen miles east of Toronto. Although on only one-and-a-quarter acres of land, Glenmaple resembled more a southern plantation than a clinic for emotionally disturbed patients. A maple-lined driveway swept up to the house, which was graced by tall white columns.

By the time it was remodeled and refurnished to accommodate four patients, three staff members, and a family of four, we were about $20,000 in debt. Vincent Lamping, my brother-in-law, covered the thousand-dollar down payment with his veteran's allowance and my father had mortgaged his farm for $6,000 to close the deal. Long before the first patient arrived, I sensed some anxiety from the bank, the T. Eaton Company (who redecorated the house), several smaller creditors, and both sides of the family. I prepared the announcement of our little clinic's opening for the medical profession in the Toronto area and we braced ourselves for the expected deluge of patients.

Glenmaple had brought together a few people whose warmth, energy, ingenuity and enthusiasm were to keep the clinic and later clinical ventures going for many years. Our household consisted of my wife, myself, our two children under three, my aunt Jessie, who was to be cook, a nurse named Mary Epp, and her husband, who was a dental student.

Mary Epp had answered our advertisement for a head nurse. She was present when we admitted our first patient and she stayed to work with us for the next twenty-nine years. In the beginning, she was our one and only nurse. Initially the position was attractive to her because it included room and board for both her and her husband. Her ability to remain calm in any kind of crisis compensated for much of our collective lack of experience. She was also singularly immune to the manipulative skills of the patients, besides being blunt, honest, unafraid, and kind. She came from the west and her distinctive laughter began with a whoop of joy as fresh and uninhibited as the prairie wind. Payday often meant little more than a new book entry that more was owed to her, but this did not affect her attitude. At least we all managed to eat. From the start, she was responsible for instituting a policy of reliance on good nursing rather than pills. Her fearlessness was reassuring to the patients as well as to the rest of us and was later communicated to the nurses she chose to work with her. At a time when caring for drunks was no more popular among nurses than it was among physicians, she did more to change this attitude within her profession than any other person I know.

I invited my aunt, Jessie Oliver, who was in her late fifties and had already had quite a remarkable career working for the Evangelism and Social Service Department of the United Church, to come and work with us. She had been a superintendent of schools for delinquent girls, a frontier missionary, a lecturer, and a champion of the downtrodden. A rather stern attitude toward overindulgence and a personal belief in abstinence from alcohol made her rather ambivalent about her new situation, but she rose to the challenge with courage, determination, and an unshakeable belief in the value of all good works. Our patients would be as special to her as the Armenian boys she had brought to our farm years earlier. Vincent joined us in October to keep an eye on his investment, as well as to serve as bookkeeper, male nurse, caretaker, driver, gardener, and just about anything else that didn't interfere with his weekend courting. Above all, he was unfailingly cheerful.

Our first three patients, however, did little to reassure us that we were in the right business. The first was a woman whose reputation was known to just about everyone but us. We later learned that there was a story in AA circles that when she had first gone to a meeting, not only had she failed to find sobriety herself but she had influenced eleven men there to get drunk. I was never able to confirm that particular story, but I soon learned that she was a very aggressive operator indeed, drunk or sober. Fortunately for us, she was not completely intoxicated on arrival and appeared to be just as astonished at finding our kind of clinic as we were at receiving this kind of patient. Lacking any other plan, we restricted treatment to cutting off her alcoholic intake, and giving her lots of attention and plenty of Aunt Jessie's good food, a basic formula for initiating treatment that we really haven't had to change much over the years. When she left a few days later she still seemed somewhat puzzled by her experience, although not, as we soon found out, seriously impressed with the need for abstinence. At least she did help to spread the word about our clinic.

Patient Number Two had been sobered up repeatedly in any place that would take him. He recognized at once that we were a bunch of amateurs, so he appointed himself a consultant for his own treatment. Among his many unusual characteristics was a tendency to lose his false teeth in the early stages of a drinking bout. As a testament to his persuasive powers, he even managed on a repeat visit to convince Vincent that the bottle of Three-Star Hennessy in his possession was for Aunt Jessie!

The outstanding characteristic of patient Number Three was that he would pick fights with two or three policemen at a time when he was drunk. At these times he was truly formidable; the rest of the time he was a gentleman. The telephone rang one evening about a month after we had opened and I recognized the voice of patient Number Two. He said that he had been talking with Number Three, who was drunk again and it was rumored that he was on his way to beat me up. I was supposed to have made some uncomplimentary remarks about him. Realizing that "Toothless" had also been drinking, and knowing that he liked stirring up trouble, I could guess where the rumor had started.

But I had no illusions about Number Three's ability to carry out his threat, so I called a hasty staff conference with my wife, Vincent, and Mary Epp. We decided that Number Three wouldn't hit a woman, so the two Marys waited by the front door for his arrival. I had prepared a hypodermic needle full of the strongest dosage of sedative I felt could be safely given, and Vincent stood in the opposite corner with a baseball bat. As soon as Number Three blasted through the door, Mary Epp started talking so fast he became completely confused. He didn't realize at first that she was undoing the belt on his trousers at the same time. As his pants began to fall, he grabbed them with one hand, thereby exposing his arm for the injection, which Mary quickly administered. Vincent never had to use the bat, because our patient was sound asleep in a few minutes. He stayed that way until the next morning. I spent the entire night with him as a precaution against further trouble. Our medical procedures have improved considerably since then.

Over the ensuing months the patient load at the little clinic gradually increased — and so did the problems. If these were sick people, they certainly didn't act like any others I had known. I had been trained to recognize an illness by a characteristic set of signs and symptoms, and to proceed with whatever treatment was indicated. But these patients seemed to have no consistent pattern of symptoms. Some arrived drunk, some shaky, some with enlarged livers, some seeing visions, and a few having convulsions. Their only common denominator was that they were problem drinkers. They shared no common personality characteristics, although most were understandably worried about their condition. Some were aggressive, outgoing people with successful business or professional careers, others hadn't made a success of anything. Some were abnormally neat and others very untidy. Many were gentle and shy when sober and exactly the opposite when drunk, while others remained consistently pleasant or unpleasant whether they were drunk or sober. They came from widely different social settings and ethnic backgrounds. I was mystified by my inability to find any useful guidelines in the medical literature, and I felt very much on my own. At the same time I was increasingly excited that I was just beginning to investigate a wholly unexplored health and social problem. (I became so impressed with the need for further research and clinical guidelines that I have concentrated on it ever since.)

Our immediate concern at the clinic was to find a way of sobering up these people quickly. With two children under three and a maiden aunt under the same roof as our patients, I soon ruled out any notions of "tapering off." We had no alternative but to try to cope with whatever situation or problem appeared to be in most urgent need of attention each day. From the beginning we insisted on abrupt withdrawal, and to hell with the consequences.

In those early months I had the good fortune to encounter an old army friend who had just completed his American board examination in psychiatry. He mentioned that alcoholic intoxication was being treated in one or two centers in the U.S. by an intravenous injection of insulin and glucose. I seized on the news with delight. At last, here was a treatment I knew something about from my service days. The technique we employed at Glenmaple was to use a fifty-c.c. syringe which, when filled with a fifty-percent glucose solution plus the insulin, measured over a foot in length from the needle to the head of the plunger. The patients quickly labeled this fearful gadget "the gun," and we just as quickly learned to assure them of its benefits in advance (but not before one patient tried to dive out the window when he saw it). The results were usually satisfactory, and when we achieved the desired reaction, the patient would find that his craving for alcohol was replaced about an hour later with a healthier hunger for food. With the injection, a noisy, uncooperative patient soon became more manageable. The chief disadvantage of the treatment was the need for constant supervision by a physician and a nurse skilled in monitoring and responding to the patient's insulin reactions for about two hours afterward. But since we were starting out with few patients and plenty of time, this was no problem.

Another of our immediate concerns in those early days of our clinical work was that we weren't making enough money at the tiny Glenmaple Clinic to meet family needs. It was as a result of this that I became involved in industrial-health work. I was hired to set up the Industrial Medical Department for the Christie Brown Bakery in Toronto in 1946, and subsequently did the same for A. Kimball Limited, Noxzema of Canada, and Highland Dairy Limited. What was important to me was the fact that this was the only branch of medicine I could find that was primarily concerned with maintaining and promoting health, rather than treating disease. And I was honoring my promise not to forget my fellow workers at Inco.

The World Health Organization had held their inaugural meeting in San Francisco in 1946, and had come up with a definition of health that had greatly impressed me: "A state of complete physical, mental, and social well-being, and not merely the absence of disease or infirmity." I applied this definition as well as I could in my examination of patients and in my health-care counseling. Some of the employees at Christie Brown had recently arrived from the Maritime provinces, and I discovered that most of them were in good physical condition, psychologically and emotionally fairly well adjusted, but without friends. Some of them had no close friends at all in Toronto, did not associate with their co-workers in off-hours, and rarely knew anyone else at the rooming houses where they lived. To help them remain productive, healthy, and emotionally well adjusted, I felt that I had to encourage them to develop new friendships with people in Toronto. As I became more aware of the social problems affecting alcoholics, in particular, I realized just how important this counseling was in the prevention and treatment of addiction.

One thing often leads to another: one result of my work in the field of industrial medicine and health was my involvement over the ensuing years with the American Association of Industrial Physicians and Surgeons (now the American Occupational Health Association). Through the association, I once had dinner with the chief physician for the head office of the General Motors Corporation. During our conversation I recounted an incident about a Toronto doctor who had told me that he had succeeded in saving a patient's life, in spite of an extremely critical clinical problem.

My older dinner companion smiled and was quiet for a moment. Then he surprised me by saying, "No physician has ever saved a life yet, only postponed death. The most that any physician can do is make it possible for patients to live a little longer, in better health, and sometimes to better purpose. As physicians, we should avoid such grandiose postures as claims to saving lives."

Aside from my industrial-medicine practice I tried at the beginning of my career to maintain a small general practice in the nearby village of Highland Creek. I hoped to earn extra money by seeing patients in the evenings, and Mary agreed that I would operate the office on a trial basis, even though it meant giving up most of the meager leisure time we had together. The experiment lasted for only a few months, because the revenue did not meet the costs. The final straw for Mary came when a young patient in the latter stages of pregnancy required immediate hospital attention. The patient had to be transported by ambulance but had no money to pay for one, so I "loaned" her the necessary twenty dollars. Mary was sympathetic to the girl's needs, and she wasn't angry but, as our financial situation was precarious, she convinced me that the office in Highland Creek had to be closed.

Our experiences at Glenmaple continued to grow in number as the list of patients passing through our doors grew. There were always new surprises. Once, after spending a long evening with a severely intoxicated patient, I was surprised to be greeted by him the next morning with, "Who the hell are you?" From similar incidents we came to accept "blackouts" — the patient's forgetting of events during intoxication — as a common symptom.

Some of our Glenmaple patients had a surprising knowledge of sedative drugs. They could discuss color, dosage, and relative effectiveness with considerable authority, and they were eager to tell us which drug worked best for them. They usually described the exact dosage with special care. A retired businessman gave me a careful seminar on the merits of the barbiturate, sodium amytal. He stressed that it was necessary for him to control his own dosage to maintain the fine balance between unbearable tension and disabling sedation. According to his own analysis, he drank uncontrollably only when he was careless about the dosage and did not maintain that balance.

Barbiturate addiction had not been mentioned at any stage of my undergraduate or postgraduate training, and sodium amytal had been popular as a prescribed drug in both the psychiatric and general hospitals where I had trained. In spite of some vague doubts I wrote out the prescription for him. About ten days later I had a call from his wife, who was very displeased with both of us. She reported that her husband was drunk all the time on sodium amytal, which he had preferred to alcohol for years.

I learned several things in a hurry that day: 1) that barbiturates can be addicting; 2) that barbiturate intoxication is more difficult to treat than alcohol intoxication, the withdrawal reaction lasts longer and is more violent; and 3) that I had to be particularly cautious about giving an addict what he or she asked for. I also realized that I should always have a chat with the addict's partner or family whenever possible.

In spite of some erratic success in coping with these kinds of acute conditions, we had a bigger problem: most of our patients soon got drunk again after our treatment and we had to repeat the whole performance over again. When I tried to find some explanation for these frustrating relapses I encountered a great deal of knowing nods and smug comments from my medical associates, mostly of the "I told you so" variety.

I continued to seek information from my colleagues, and also began to explore the Fellowship of Alcoholics Anonymous, an organization which had been developing across North America. Although the fellowship had started very slowly in the 1930s, membership numbered in the thousands and groups had been established in many large cities by the time I sought them out in 1946. I was puzzled and intrigued by this organization's structure and aims. I began to attend the meetings of the first AA group at 1170 Yonge Street in Toronto. As I listened to speaker after speaker I realized that they were talking about my kind of patient, but with an important difference. Many of them no longer suffered relapses, and some recounted not only years of unbroken abstinence but "contented sobriety."

This was fascinating to me. Were these individuals really being honest? Could they successfully replace a life of drinking with a life of abstinence because they actually preferred it? Were they truly motivated to change their lives by more than fear of the consequences? If this were indeed so, I could begin to appreciate one of the reasons why most professional advice failed to have any effect on these people. I remembered one gruff old doctor who had summarized his frustration with such patients: "I told the damn fool over and over again that he was ruining his liver, but he wouldn't listen. So we buried him last week."

I usually sat at the back of the AA meetings to observe the interplay between the members as well as the speakers — their laughter, their easy friendliness, and their general freedom from embarrassment. Their behavior was in marked contrast to the resentment, lying, alibis, and cover-ups that characterized their reactions to the attitudes of the outside community. I recognized all kinds of personalities in their ranks, which further convinced me that no particular personality type or psychological disability could be considered stereotypical in these individuals.

One of our Glenmaple patients had relapsed after being dry in AA for eleven months. His was an intriguing case, for he had an unusual personal and family history, including three brothers with alcohol problems. I reviewed his history with him, trying to relate some of his childhood experiences to his adult behavior, and he was delighted. "No one has ever explained these things before. I can see it all so clearly, my drinking problems are over!" he exclaimed. He was still elated over his new insights when he was discharged a few days later and I enjoyed the comfortable feeling of a job well done. To celebrate his victory over his past, however, he got drunk that same night and was readmitted a few days later. When we resumed our conversation, this time with somewhat dampened enthusiasm, I said, "I don't know what kept you sober for eleven months in AA, but I suggest you forget about our discussion and go back there to find out."

I think the first clinical lesson I learned from AA derived from their firm belief that the uncontrollable drinkers who made up their membership had to stop drinking permanently. In those years some psychiatrists opposed this conclusion, insisting that controlled drinking could be resumed once the alcoholic's underlying psychological problems had been resolved. Other professionals, who continued to provide psychotherapy to alcoholic patients while they continued to drink, agreed with them. For my own part, I have yet to see any conclusive evidence that an alcoholic can become a social drinker; I know of a countless number of cases where many tried — with disastrous results.

By 1947 I had worked out a method of estimating insulin dosage for the "gun" treatment and was anxious to better understand how and why it worked. Professor George Lucas of the department of pharmacology at the University of Toronto was an old friend whom I had known as a teacher and as an instructor. When Dr. Lucas heard my story he introduced me to Ward Smith, a biochemist doing research on blood-alcohol levels for his Ph.D. thesis. Since the medico-legal problems associated with drinking were about as controversial as the clinical ones, we were both happy to find someone with whom we could share plans, problems, and dreams. It was also the beginning of a deep friendship that lasted until Ward's death from lung cancer twenty years later. Neither of us realized in those early days that our partnership and friendship would lead to a number of exciting adventures in the exploration of alcohol-related behaviors.

At Glenmaple, we were beginning to work out a routine for the care of patients, but our finances remained extremely precarious. The husband of one of our patients, who was an astute businessman, tactfully raised the subject of our financial situation one evening. He shook his head, frowned, looked around the place and then asked, "Where do you do your banking?" When I told him, he said, "You need a loan immediately. Go to my bank at eleven o'clock tomorrow morning and have a talk with the manager." If not for the help of this stranger we would have gone bankrupt long before the end of our first year. His banker was anxious to co-operate but he worried about us (with good reason) throughout the nine years that we dealt with him.

In any event, my wife's enthusiasm for the Glenmaple enterprise was waning markedly. When an overloaded septic tank was added to our problems, little doubt remained in her mind. But for the sturdy resilience of Mary's Irish and Pennsylvania Dutch background, she would have cracked completely from the combined daily responsibilities of appeasing our creditors, meeting the payroll, buying groceries, and changing diapers. To compound the problem, Vincent brought his new bride, Helen, into our home in May of that year, and our second daughter, Linda, was born in October. We already knew that a baby crying at night did little to soothe a patient with the shakes, and that the older children were becoming spoiled by gifts from a never-ending succession of new "uncles" and "aunts." After nearly nine solid months of emotionally demanding work with so many people and no holidays at all, we were ready for a break.

Early in 1947 we were all reaching the same conclusion. A change was needed. At this point, one of our patients, who had more reason to be impressed by the sincerity of our efforts than by their success, unexpectedly came to our rescue. He was a tall, handsome, middle-aged business executive whose competence and shrewdness between drinking bouts compensated for his periodic relapses. "Mac" pointed out that we were too small ever to achieve financial stability and that we either had to get out of the treatment business altogether or go into it on a larger scale. With some misgivings from my little gang, most of whom were still owed a considerable amount in back wages, we decided to follow the second course. He promptly set out to find someone to finance a larger operation, while I began discussions with health officials, looking for another more suitable property.

CHAPTER SIX

The Shadow Brook Period

The Ontario Ministry of Health and the Bell family were beginning to get more acquainted with each other during this, our second series of discussions. The ministry decided that a larger clinical service for alcohol addicts could best operate with a private sanitarium license. (The only other private sanitarium in the province was the Homewood Sanitarium in Guelph.) All we needed was money and a place to operate. To help us out, Mac contacted a prominent financier, Mr. A. Bruce Davidson, who was willing to discuss backing such a project, but deferred a final decision until we had located a suitable property. For the second time, Mary and I began touring the city and surrounding countryside, this time looking for a building large enough to accommodate about twenty-five patients. This meant that we looked at homes originally built for the wealthy and usually located in zones restricted to residential use. We did find one large estate that would have served our purpose in a suitably zoned area, but when the neighbors learned of our plans they quickly formed a syndicate to buy the property and hold on to it until we were safely located elsewhere.

Then we found Shadow Brook, a forty-acre estate on Finch Avenue in North York, about twelve miles north-west of downtown Toronto. It was a large Spanish-style home amid acres of lawns, flowerbeds, and trees. The Don River, which flowed through the property, had formerly been dammed up, and the name Shadow Brook derived from the reflection of the trees in the water above the dam.

The Ministry of Health agreed to give us a license to operate a private sanitarium for male patients only. Although we had not encountered any particular difficulties having both men and women under the same roof at Glenmaple, the ministry would not grant us permission to operate a mixed treatment center, since we lacked the facilities to separate the sexes. Bruce Davidson agreed to purchase the estate on these terms. He also bought most of the existing furnishings, like the paintings and oriental rugs, which provided us with the richest clinical setting that we could possibly imagine.

There were still a few problems to be ironed out, however. Township officials were not convinced that a private sanitarium was in the best interests of the area, nor did the neighbors, who held a meeting and invited me to attend. Upon our assurance that only alcoholic patients would be admitted, and not all kinds of "crazy" people, they were somewhat reassured. But they also insisted that we give the township a written guarantee that we would limit the number of admissions and assure the community that they would not be disturbed. One neighbor helped our cause considerably by suggesting to the others that it was likely that under our auspices there would be less drinking on the property than there had been at some of the parties they had attended there in the past.

We took possession of Shadow Brook in December 1947. Vincent, our business manager, and his bride, Helen, who acted as our secretary, moved in first. They fully enjoyed having the whole place to themselves for those few weeks until January 1948. They entertained their many friends in fine style as much as possible, until just before the first patients arrived.

Besides bringing with us the new techniques we had

developed at Glenmaple for treating alcoholic intoxication, Mary Epp had selected and trained a small, dedicated nursing staff and we had a following of loyal former patients in varying degrees of sobriety. But we were also convinced that although we believed firmly in the importance of a warm, informal environment for our patients and staff, something more had to be added to our treatment plan.

Actually, one of the nurses hired at Shadow Brook carried our convictions of a warm, caring environment a bit too far. There were two parts to the complex and they were connected by an underground tunnel. Those patients who did not require careful supervision at night were housed in quarters apart from the main building. The new nurse began with us on the night shift, and used to make her rounds of the less-distressed men after midnight. We soon began to notice that these patients were behaving much more serenely and contentedly since the new nurse had been hired. We became suspicious, and finally, after some discreet investigating, we discovered that she had a very healthy sexual appetite. (At the same time we realized that sex seemed to be a wonderfully effective method of tranquilizing patients.) We were forced to let her go, however, before Shadow Brook developed a reputation as a house of ill repute.

I was still unsure how our new clinic could enhance the recovery program I had observed at AA, but I knew too that there were many patients who were unable to benefit from the AA program or who had stubbornly refused to join. Were these people inevitably doomed to alcoholism, or could other solutions for their recovery be found? As a first step toward the development of better treatment plans, I decided that improved communication was needed between staff and patients. We needed a common language.

The nurses took the history of all the patients when they were admitted, based on a comprehensive form that I had prepared. They cared for the patients through the difficult first few days, and were in a favorable position to overcome any defensive thinking at this crucial stage in the patient-staff relationship. Most patients were unhappy about being with us during the early stages of their treatment, and we knew that if we failed to overcome their resistance at this point, we would not be able to initiate their recovery from addiction. The nurses played a vital role from the beginning to bridge this gap between the patients and the people around them.

The total fee for three to four weeks of accommodation, medical and nursing services, meals, medication, and health counseling was $400. The patients paid for this themselves because there was no insurance coverage of any kind for alcoholism treatment at that time. Since most of our patients realized that the cost of their treatment was less than the amount they spent on alcohol each year, we did not usually encounter difficulties in collecting our fees.

In clinical circles, alcoholism, however one defined it, was still commonly believed to be a symptom of other disorders. Following this idea to its logical conclusion implied that a drinking problem would automatically disappear when its underlying cause was identified and corrected. Based on what I had heard from AA speakers and from talks with our own patients, I did not believe this conclusion. At first this led to some confusion for our patients when I used the term "disease" to describe alcohol addiction. Another reason for seeking a different common ground for dialogue with patients came from my experience in the army when I had learned that practically every psychiatric term in professional or common use was considered degrading by those affected. No one, for example, enjoys being referred to as "immature" or "inadequate." One of our rules at Glenmaple, therefore, had been to avoid psychiatric labels as much as possible in referring to patients or while talking to them. We found that this was a particularly sound policy in dealing with people who were very sensitive about their problems when they came to us.

In my contact with patients up to that time, both in the army and at Glenmaple, I had found that most were ready to acknowledge that physical illness was an acceptable part of life. It could be counted on to stimulate interest and care from the clinical professions, as well as sympathetic attention from the rest of the community.

Impairment in mental and emotional well-being, however, was not so well understood. Unpleasant or disabling states of tension were often considered by the patient to be his or her own fault — the product of his or her imagination, a shameful sign of weakness, or the first step toward "the loony bin." Many people believed that psychiatrists and psychologists worked only with insane patients, and that treatment would be carried out in prison-like hospitals. In this regard the victims of disabling states of tension or depression were less fortunate than those who suffered physical pain.

But if patients had difficulty appreciating the nature of mental well-being, this was nothing compared to their confusion over social well-being. In this connection I began to consider the possible clinical implications of loneliness. I felt that the term had significance specifically for social beings who communicated effectively with others of their kind on a regular basis and who developed rewarding interdependent relationships with them. In my examination of industrial employees I had routinely begun to look for loneliness and to consider it just as indicative of an impairment in health as other disabling states of pain or tension could be. I began to consider the barriers to communication that contributed to loneliness, both within the community and the person, and the possible means of removing them. Accordingly, I trained the industrial nurses with whom I worked to think in terms of a balanced consideration of physical, mental, and social well-being, and to be as concerned about loneliness as they were about pain or tension.

While working with our first alcoholic patients, I had already begun to consider how an impairment in health in all three areas could affect an individual. Health rather than disease provided the theme for our programs. Although patients might disagree about whether or not they had a disease, they were usually prepared to admit that there was some room for improvement in their physical, mental, and social well-being, if not in all three. I hoped that if my uncontrolled drinkers could be sold on the prospect of rewards for improved well-being, they might be able to accept abstinence as the vital first step.

With these thoughts in mind, I established our first "school" for patients as the next, or second, phase of treatment, after they had recovered from their intoxicated state. The "curriculum" was repeated every three weeks. As soon as the patients were able to be up and around, they were invited to sit in. Some of our chronic cases were intrigued when the blackboard joined the "gun" as one of our regular clinical tools. This program of individual and group instruction and counseling has remained an important part of our treatment plan ever since.

Some of our patients needed more schooling than others; many just needed to be directed to new vocations. We admitted a lawyer to Shadow Brook who at one time had been posted to the British embassy in Washington. He claimed that this experience had significantly contributed to his personal alcohol problem, since one of his responsibilities had been to represent the embassy at an endless succession of cocktail parties. On one occasion, he had just returned from such a gathering when he was asked by his superior to turn around and go to another one. When he expressed some reluctance in performing his role as the embassy's convivial representative, the ambassador said to him, "Your only regret should be that you have but one liver to give to the service of His Majesty."

Other physicians soon joined our medical staff on a part-time basis, including one doctor who has since gone on to outstanding achievements in the addiction field. Dr. Harold Kalant is now a professor of pharmacology at the University of Toronto and director of biobehavioural studies for the Addiction Research Foundation of Ontario. From time to time an AA member acted as a visiting lecturer, and between all of us we gave the patients something new to think about at our meetings. To round out our educational program, we selected films on various aspects of mental health. In 1951, an article by Sidney Katz appeared in *Maclean's* magazine entitled "Gordon Bell's School for Sobriety." This was the first popular media coverage of our operations to appear in Canada, and it led both to greater public interest in our activities, and to an immediate increase in requests for me to speak to various groups.

We also searched for non-medical means of relieving tension. Mary Epp had learned various techniques in the art of progressive relaxation, introducing another component to our treatment plan, and one comparable to that of Dorothy Madgett at the psychological retraining center at Brampton. Mary eventually became very proficient, and the relaxation period after lunch became famous for her incantation, "Let go . . . let go more . . . and more . . . and more!" Many years later, an elderly patient participating in the session, who was still coming out of his alcoholic fog, exclaimed, "Wasn't it lovely when the nurse led us all in prayer!"

Since we knew that barbiturate drugs and other sedatives could be particularly addictive to our patients, we decided to develop a sedative of our own that would be safe in two ways: first, it would be a private prescription, not available to anyone else; and second, it would taste so horrible that no one would want to repeat the dose anyway. I broached the idea with Ward Smith, who was working in the pharmacology department at the University of Toronto, and he responded with enthusiasm. We arranged to spend a Saturday at the lab to test out an assortment of concoctions. Only later did I appreciate that part of Ward's enthusiasm was owed to his plan that I should be the guinea pig while he, with eyebrows arched and sporting a fiendish grin, acted the role of the mad scientist. We tried several mixtures, all utterly revolting, until we finally agreed that we had the right one. The sedative ingredients were chloral hydrate and valerian, combined with other nauseating substances that were so overpowering it was impossible to tell whether or not the mixture contained sedative at all. Initially we prepared three grades — full-strength, half-strength, and placebo. The mixtures were all an identical dirty-brown color, and the first startled patients who received it promptly dubbed it "bug juice." We congratulated ourselves that none of our patients could become addicted to any sedative they had received from us — or so we thought at first. I was so certain that the patients would take only the minimum required to ease the shakes that I issued a small bottle to each one to take as he felt the need. My respect for the power of addiction profoundly increased when one group of patients went on a bug-juice binge.

We admitted a very interesting assortment of patients in the first few months of 1948. Some of our more prominent guests had once been entertained as respectable citizens by the owners of Shadow Brook in the old days before we took over, and these people felt right at home. In spite of the fact that our luxurious setting soon gave us the reputation of catering only to the rich, the majority of our patients came from middle-class backgrounds. Interestingly, too, social status seemed to have little effect on the natural development of new relationships in the hospital. And the patients indicated that they considered these new friendships important.

Soon after sending out our announcements of the Shadow Brook opening, I learned from a worried former classmate that a physician had openly denounced me at a meeting of the Toronto Academy of Medicine. According to him, any clinic for addicts as sumptuously furnished as ours had to be crooked. Many years later, Dr. Victor Johnston, who had organized the Canadian College of General Practitioners, asked me, "Do you remember when Dr. Kirk Lyon, then the president of the Ontario Medical

Association, and I came to see you after you opened Shadow Brook? We were an OMA committee sent to investigate your operation, because it was rumored that you were some kind of medical racketeer out to make a fortune from sobering up wealthy drunks."

"What kind of racket did you find?" I asked, and he answered, "We didn't find any."

Actually, this investigation served to establish a sound reputation for us with the Ontario College of Physicians and Surgeons, as well as with the OMA and the Canadian Medical Association. The real truth was that my annual salary never reached as high as $10,000 during the Shadow Brook period.

Our program and facilities impressed the patients as well, I believe. During the first two years of our operations, we had discussions with them and they made it quite clear that they wanted some kind of follow-up service to sustain their new friendships and to continue their recovery. It was a novel experience for them to realize that our respect for their intelligence and judgment was not affected by our knowledge of their alcoholism. They were also amazed that they were consulted concerning plans for a continuing-therapy program. Realizing that I was already on call on a twenty-four-hour basis, and particularly busy during the day, a group of them suggested that I let them plan the follow-up phase.

At first I had some misgivings about what their combined ingenuity might produce. All of them had already demonstrated great skill in manipulating their environment to accommodate their addiction, and I was well aware that the continuing power of an uncontrolled dependence on alcohol could thwart the best of intentions. I was, therefore, particularly pleased when the patients came back with the idea of forming a club of Shadow Brook alumni, which would also include their families and friends. To emphasize the Shadow Brook theme of physical, mental, and social well-being, they suggested that it be called the Three Point Club. Some of them already belonged to athletic and social clubs, and they knew how to start one, what type of charter to obtain, how to collect fees, and many other things about which the rest of us were completely uninformed. They decided to meet weekly on Wednesday nights for special follow-up instruction and to plan other social activities, like movies, etc., for the weekends. The patients elected their own officers, paid rent to Shadow Brook, and arranged for all of their activities, social and therapeutic. I acted as consultant and was a frequent guest lecturer in the Wednesday-evening program.

In those six years the Three Point Club of Shadow Brook held garden parties, banquets, concerts, movies, dances, and New Year's Eve celebrations that rivaled anything in Shadow Brook history — and all without booze! The house had been designed for large-scale entertaining, and the living-room, dining-room, and recreation area could easily accommodate a hundred or more people. I will never forget the astonished expression on the face of one new patient who staggered in about 10:00 P.M. in the middle of a buffet dinner and dance. I don't know whether he thought he had come to the wrong address or if the revelry was a new form of treatment.

We finally got around to doing some serious research at Shadow Brook as well. One of our first projects was to set up a controlled study on the effectiveness of the insulin-glucose method of treating alcoholic intoxication. Ward Smith worked out the research plan with other members of the staff at the university's pharmacology department and I prepared for the clinical problems that could arise if an untreated drunk patient became unmanageable. I was to administer to every patient on admission an injection of one of five types — insulin with glucose and vitamins, insulin and glucose, glucose alone, vitamins in saline, and saline alone. We decided randomly which patient received which injection. Ward and a young intern, Dr. George McBroom, carried out a comprehensive examination of each patient before the treatment, and then repeated the exam six hours later.

When the study was completed we reviewed our findings with Ward's chief, Dr. J. K. W. Ferguson, who was at that time professor and head of the pharmacology department. Ward listed the results on the blackboard, with ratings for improvement, and I produced the code to relate results to treatment. We were excited to find a significant improvement using the insulin-glucose method, and the results still stand out as one of the highlights of those early days. The old "gun" really worked!

The end result justified our difficulties in carrying out the study, but none of us was sorry when it came to an end. Ward's periodic outbursts of profanity only emphasized the difficulties he encountered when some intoxicated patients decided not to co-operate with his carefully planned tests. My amusement at this hardly lightened his mood, but he perked up noticeably when I ran into problems of my own with those patients who showed little improvement. On those occasions, his happy expression indicated the study had been worthwhile after all. Ward and George McBroom later published their study in the September 1950 issue of the *Canadian Medical Association Journal*, and I made plans to prepare another article outlining the technique of administering the insulin-glucose treatment.

As a result of our study, Dr. Ken Ferguson became seriously interested in addiction, and he became a significant force in research, treatment, and education in the field throughout Ontario and beyond. In the end, Ken Ferguson became an invaluable consultant, supporter, and friend through a succession of very trying experiences.

Since the College of Physicians and Surgeons was the custodian of medical ethics and practice for our profession, I decided to make a consistent effort to keep them informed of all phases of our work and to seek their advice before undertaking any unusual projects in research or treatment. I received help from Dr. Robert Noble, who was executive secretary of the college at that time. He listened carefully to my account of our treatment plan and our research into the insulin-glucose method of interrupting alcoholic intoxication. He concurred with my hunch that we should be extremely careful in preparing a paper describing our methods. He reminded me that I was practising in a very unpopular field, one which had attracted few physicians in the province. In his opinion, some of the physicians willing to treat patients for drunkenness were operating on the fringe of acceptable medical practice. Many of them were often careless in their administration of any type of treatment. Since the insulin-glucose treatment required skilled supervision for prolonged periods, he doubted that many of those who might like to try our method would take the trouble to carry it out safely. Dr. Noble warned that in the event of a disaster resulting from careless administration, I would receive full blame, unless I had covered every possible contingency in my report. Finally, he advised me to take my time and to prepare the article anyway. I was so impressed with his reasoning that the paper took two more years to prepare before it was eventually published in the June 1951 issue of the *Canadian Medical Association Journal.*

One of the most dramatic and exciting breakthroughs at this time, however, was the development of a drug called Antabuse. In December 1948, *Time* magazine ran a brief story about a drug recently discovered in Denmark that made people sick when they drank an alcoholic beverage after taking it. The discoverer, Dr. Erik Jacobsen, recommended that all physicians planning to use the drug first try it out on themselves. I called Ward Smith in great excitement, and we wrote at once to Dr. Jacobsen about obtaining a supply. Dr. Jacobsen replied just as promptly, and by January 1949 we had our first shipment of Antabuse. In fact, I believe that this was the first shipment of the drug to cross the Atlantic; it was certainly the first to reach our part of the North American continent.

Ward and I were intrigued by Dr. Jacobsen's suggestion that physicians should experience their own Antabuse/alcohol reaction before prescribing the drug, and we readily agreed to do so. We also felt that observers ought to be present as well to note our reactions. To that end we invited Drs. Ken Ferguson and George Lucas from the university's department of pharmacology and John Dewan and Ab Miller from the Toronto Psychiatric Hospital. Ward and I took the recommended dosage of Antabuse for four days to prepare ourselves. I experienced no disturbing symptoms from the drug itself, except for some moderate intestinal cramps and a slight metallic taste in my mouth. All the observers were on hand for the test, and Mary Epp was prepared for any nursing emergency. Since I was somewhat heavier than Ward, we decided that I would take three ounces of whisky and he would consume two ounces. Ken Ferguson checked our blood pressure, heart rate, and respiration; George Lucas poured the drinks.

My memory of the next few hours is a bit vague. At first, apparently, I became as flushed as a beet from the waist up. I remember feeling a suffocating sensation in my chest. Then I suddenly turned very pale and felt nauseated. What I most clearly recall, however, was the expression on Ken Ferguson's face when he checked my blood pressure and found that my diastolic (lower) reading was zero and that my pulse was occasionally disappearing. Since he was a cool, dispassionate medical scientist, it was rare indeed to see him register astonishment at anything. I was told afterward that everyone present was thoroughly impressed with the effects of Antabuse and I quickly discarded any doubts that the drug might not work. Ward's reaction to Antabuse and alcohol was much the same as mine. The only difference was that he developed a worse headache than I did afterward. He said that if we didn't know before whether or not Antabuse worked, "We bloody well know now!"

Five hours later we were generally back to normal and

able to discuss our experiences. In the light of our reactions to the potent mixture we felt that it could be hazardous to follow another recommendation of the Danish doctor, which was to allow the Antabuse-treated patient to discover for himself how the drug would force him to stop drinking. Since some of our patients could toss back large amounts of whisky at a gulp, we decided that the reactions to the drug would be too severe for the unsuspecting drinker. So we instituted a policy of considering the Antabuse/alcohol test a prerequisite for most of our patients before they took the drug on a regular basis.

We ruled out those patients who already suffered from heart disease, cirrhosis of the liver, and organic brain damage. We gradually modified this rule in later years as we became more aware of the special hazards of continuous drinking in patients with life-threatening disabilities. Some of these patients were among the first to be given Antabuse without an Antabuse/alcohol test, but we explained to them very carefully what would happen if they drank while taking the drug, and that the disadvantages of taking it were far outweighed by the benefits of not drinking. They could not afford more physical damage from continued drinking. By 1954 we had totally discontinued the test before prescribing Antabuse, in favor of carefully explaining the possible effects of drinking while taking it.

Many of our patients complained of side-effects from the drug, ranging from drowsiness, weakness, an unpleasant taste, and body odor to impotence. Since these discomforts persuaded many of them to discontinue its use, we gradually reduced the dosage and continued to search for alternatives. It took several years before we came upon a substitute.

Ward and I continued to test our own reactions to alcohol daily after our initial experience with Antabuse. We found that we had a definitely decreasing reaction to alcohol, and after five days the medication's effect had worn off completely. We were not surprised to find that most

Antabuse patients who decided to resume their drinking simply stopped taking the drug for five or more days and then returned to their old habits. Only a few could not wait that long.

One of the first patients to receive Antabuse was a restless and aggressive stockbroker who suddenly announced to us, after four days on the drug, that he had urgent business to take care of in Chicago. Since he was one of the patients who had not had the benefit of an Antabuse/alcohol test, I made a special effort to convince him of the importance of not undertaking one on his own. Two days later I received a call from a physician in Chicago who identified himself as a hotel doctor. He said he was very concerned about the condition of one of the hotel's guests. The man kept mumbling my name in connection with some new drug. He added that never in his many years of practice had he come across a patient in such condition. The man smelled powerfully of booze and of something else the doctor could not identify. The patient was flushed over most of his upper body, and his heart rate and blood pressure were wildly abnormal.

I explained the relationship between Antabuse and alcohol and began to recommend the proper treatment for the man, but the doctor interrupted me.

"Thanks, Doctor," he said, "but don't discuss treatment with me. This bird is going to the hospital."

About an hour later I received a second call from Chicago, this time from a physician at one of the large hospitals. He sounded both alarmed and angry. He had never heard of any drug that produced such symptoms, and he was not pleased to find himself pioneering a new kind of therapy for a previously unknown clinical syndrome.

By this time our patient was totally unable to communicate, and the Sisters who operated the hospital wondered whether or not they should call a priest to administer the last rites to him. In all the confusion, nobody at the hospital had tried to find out if the patient was a Catholic. In their dilemma they consulted the old Irish priest who served as the hospital chaplain. He took one look at the man's flushed face, smelled his breath, and apparently said, "Only an Irishman could get that drunk," and gave him the last rites anyway.

The patient soon recovered completely, and found himself the focal point of interest in the hospital. Before he was released he made a special point of thanking the medical staff and the old priest, in spite of the fact that he was not a Catholic after all.

This was one of several incidents that led us to prepare a card to be carried by Antabuse patients explaining the nature of the drug and describing the proper treatment for Antabuse/alcohol reactions. Most of the clinics that began using the drug continued to issue a card throughout the 1950s, until physicians and other health-care providers became sufficiently aware of the drug and its effects.

Two months after we had performed our own test and instituted a clinical trial, a drug company, Ayerst, McKenna & Harrison Inc., announced that it had obtained rights for the manufacture and distribution of Antabuse in the United States and Canada. The company's literature repeated the original dosage and testing recommendations of the Danish group. We felt this could lead to some wild scenes, such as the episode in Chicago and others we had experienced, so I got in touch with the doctors who had observed Ward's and my reactions. We reviewed our cases to date, and then called Dr. Arthur Kelly, the secretary of the Canadian Medical Association, who arranged for the immediate publication of a preliminary report in a stop-the-press call to the *Canadian Medical Association Journal.*

Just two months after taking our own test, Ward and I found ourselves co-authors of an article in March 1949 on Antabuse. I was prouder of that than I had any right to be, since everyone connected with the test had co-operated on the article, and the finishing touches had been done by Dr. Kelly himself.

In April 1949 I attended the annual convention of the American Association of Industrial Physicians and Surgeons, which was held that year in Detroit. I had been involved with the group through my position as company doctor for the Toronto-based companies of Christie Brown, A. Kimball Limited, Noxzema of Canada, and Highland Dairy. I appreciated the fact that these companies wished to prevent their employees from becoming ill, rather than merely treat them once they were sick. I had been unable to attend earlier meetings in other parts of the U.S. during the Glenmaple and early Shadow Brook years, because we did not have enough money for me to travel very far. At this meeting I was particularly anxious to meet Dr. George Gehrmann, medical director of the Dupont Corporation in Wilmington, Delaware, who was chairman of the Committee on Problem Drinking. Up to that point, no other medical association had displayed interest in alcoholism as a medical condition.

I arranged to meet Dr. Gehrmann, who promptly invited me to become a member of his committee and to attend their meeting later that day. The main purpose of his committee meeting was to complete plans for a special program to be presented in general session the following day. When he learned of my recent experiences with Antabuse, he asked me to take part in the actual program and reorganized the agenda to fit me in. Since this was the first medical group in North America to hear about Antabuse, my brief report received considerable publicity.

The next day I had my first experience of speaking before a television camera, and it heralded the beginning of a lifelong association with the United States for me and our clinic. We had suddenly been catapulted into the public eye by media all over the United States and, to a lesser degree, in Canada. I had never anticipated that the conference would have such far-reaching consequences. And all this happened before we had become very sure about Antabuse, or anything else in the clinical management of alcohol problems.

All this media attention brought us one patient in particular whose experience indicated to us that Antabuse did indeed have a place in the clinical management of alcohol addiction. "Charlie" arrived from Ohio in 1950, and a wilder, rougher-looking patient would be hard to imagine. He had a gravelly, whisky-baritone voice that could be heard for blocks, short bristly hair that stood on end, shoulders like a bull, and not a tooth in his head. He roared into our clinic smelling strongly of muscatel — "Sweet Lucy" as he called it — and demanded "some of that stuff that makes drunks sick." It took quite a while to quiet Charlie down and to persuade him that a few other details had to be taken care of first, like sobering him up.

Charlie had been arrested sixty-nine times for drunkenness in his hometown alone, and had put in a few long stretches in the workhouse. He looked to be a very tough customer. In fact, he was so tough that even though he had no teeth he ate everything we gave him, including steak and peanuts. And when we gave him his Antabuse/alcohol test, his initial reaction was so mild that we wondered if the drug would work on him at all. Added to Antabuse, muscatel and beer simply made him feel good. It wasn't until I also gave him a shot of whisky that he demonstrated the usual reaction. By the time we were finished with the test, we were all quite impressed with the results — and so was Charlie. Charlie continued to use Antabuse for about five years, and he remained dry until his death from heart disease more than eighteen years later.

But we still had a long way to go to incorporate Antabuse into a comprehensive treatment program. In those early years of treating alcoholics, it was an additional tool in our efforts to introduce our patients to a rewarding life of abstinence. To solve problems with the drug's side-effects, we tried cutting down the dosage to a half- or even a quarter-tablet daily, and that corrected most of the problems. Some patients found that the lower dose did not provide a reliable deterrent to renewed drinking. Many of them quickly moved from a reduced dosage to no dosage at all. Yet those who were fortunate enough to be relatively free of side-effects were more likely to use the drug long enough to find a satisfactory formula for a life of abstinence, as Charlie did.

I remember that Antabuse treatment was very suspect in AA circles. The medical director of the Fisher Body Division of General Motors Corporation routinely referred his alcoholic employees to AA. When he became concerned about those who were not responding to the AA program, he put them on Antabuse and sent them back to AA. He told me, "For the first time they stayed sober long enough to find out what AA was all about!"

In the meantime I still contemplated the problem of those patients who could not tolerate Antabuse. Could a substitute be found, one that would not have the same unpleasant side-effects as Antabuse, and that would enable the alcoholic to buy the time necessary to develop a sober lifestyle?

The answer came at another industrial medicine meeting. I was seated at the banquet beside Dr. Dick Warmington, who was then the medical director of a plant operated by the American Cyanimid Company. He told me that he believed that many of the plant employees were having reactions similar to that of our Antabuse-treated patients when they stopped to drink a few beers on their way home from work. This sort of news was right up Ken Ferguson's alley. At that time in the early 1950s he was still a professor and the head of pharmacology at the University of Toronto. He had also recently become chairman of the Professional Advisory Board for the Alcoholism Research Foundation and was most interested in this phenomenon.

Ken obtained a supply of chemicals from the plant and began to explore methods of purifying and modifying it for possible medical use. He used two guinea pigs — himself and me. I cannot recall how many different preparations we tried, but I do remember one of them very vividly. My stomach felt as if it had been shot through with a searing bullet. Following that particular test I strongly recommended to Ken that he continue to try to find a mixture with less dramatic side-effects. He finally came up with citrated calcium carbimide, which sat gently in my stomach but was guaranteed — in my case anyway — to produce a post-drink reaction remarkably similar to that of the Antabuse/alcohol test. We conducted the tests at home with no medical supervision, but we were careful not to imbibe too large an amount of either alcohol or the preparation Ken had prepared. On one occasion, he was not as careful as I and drank a couple of martinis at a party in his home after he had taken the citrated calcium carbimide. At first he began to feel only a little uneasy, but after an hour or so he became quite alarmed: the reaction was every bit as powerful as the one produced by Antabuse and alcohol. By the time he recovered, he felt he had probably found a satisfactory substitute for Antabuse.

Ken arranged for the Lederle Drug Division of the American Cyanamid Company to prepare and market the new drug, which they called Temposil. True to his principles, Ken also arranged for the Alcoholism Research Foundation to receive any monetary rewards for his efforts. The new drug acted faster than Antabuse, had no undesirable effects on a person's breath or body odor, and was eliminated more rapidly. Most people could resume drinking only twenty-four hours after stopping Temposil and suffer few if any consequences.

We began a clinical trial in November 1955, and replaced Antabuse with Temposil, which was given to sixty-four patients up to the middle of March 1956, when Ken and I began preparing articles for the *Canadian Medical Association Journal*. Twenty-six of the patients had previously taken Antabuse, and twenty-three of those had experienced unpleasant side-effects with the drug. None of the patients in this Temposil study had any of the side-effects associated with Antabuse, although two discontinued using Temposil for other reasons, and the results of a test dose of alcohol produced results similar to those produced by the Antabuse/alcohol test. (Although Temposil was never approved for use in the United States, we continue to use it successfully today.)

With the development of drugs like Antabuse and Temposil and the sudden mushrooming of ideas that were interconnecting at a rapid rate in those heady days, I decided to pull together some ideas that had been incubating in my mind for some time.

I had continued to manipulate the jigsaw puzzle of addiction and its related problems in my mind since the Glenmaple days and often thought about the need for a clinical blueprint to help me. I awoke with a start one night in 1951, and there it was! The whole problem was revealed in all its complexity — cause and effect, interrelationships, diagnosis, and treatment. I could hardly wait to get that (what I considered) brilliant, world-shaking concept down on paper. For the next few days I wrote furiously whenever I had any spare time, but somehow the overall picture began to fade. There were also some strange gaps in reasoning that I hadn't noticed when I had my "flash."

I pulled my ideas together as well as I could, however, and took the paper down to Ken Ferguson for his comments. He read the paper very carefully, without changing expression, and then said, "Well, Gordon, this may mean something to you, but it doesn't mean a thing to me!"

I was crushed and indignant, and I asked him what was wrong with it. By the time he had finished detailing the points, I was convinced that there was very little in my blueprint that was right. I discovered that I did not know the basic principles of toxicology, that my knowledge of physiology and biochemistry was inadequate and inaccurate, that I had leaped to several totally unsupported conclusions, and that I would need to do a great deal of intensive review and homework if I wanted to publish such an article.

That fall and winter I studied whenever I could, rewrote the article several times, and finally Ken said that it was good enough to be published. Dr. Arthur Kelly, who had helped with the Antabuse report three years earlier, learned of my struggles with the "blueprint" paper and arranged for me to present it in general session at the coming annual meeting of the Canadian Medical Association. On June 12, 1952, I stood before my first large audience of fellow physicians, scared to death. My mouth was so dry that I drank almost an entire pitcher of water during the presentation. One of my former classmates commented later that I must have been full of my subject! Good, bad, or indifferent, mine was the first paper on alcoholism to be presented in general session to that august body, and it was later published in the January 1953 issue of the *Canadian Medical Association Journal.*

Looking back at my first "blueprint," my chief criticism today is that there is little advantage in trying to assess the state of drinking so exactly, and that it is difficult or impossible for a clinic to maintain effective contact with patients for four years, as I had attempted. It is also apparent that our orientation during the Shadow Brook days was overly concerned with intoxication and too little concerned with the individual's underlying dependence to provide a proper and balanced basis for a comprehensive treatment program. Although our Antabuse paper expressed concern for the powerful, controlling influence of addiction, there was little evidence at that stage of our development that the actual addiction itself was perceived as a distinct clinical problem. Rereading the blueprint paper now, I shudder to think what it must have been like when I first showed it to Ken Ferguson. I have been very suspicious of "flashes" of insight ever since.

My participation in the activities of the American

Association of Industrial Physicians and Surgeons continued. In 1951 I was appointed chairman of the Committee on Problem Drinking, and I held the position for seven years. This was a very important position for me to hold, because the association covered not only major corporations in the United States and Canada, but some in Europe and other parts of the world as well. The association's annual convention was held in April in the U.S., and for the years that I was chairman of that committee we hammered home the same basic message: "Uncontrolled drinking is primarily a health problem; deal with it first as a health problem and, if that fails, then you can take the appropriate disciplinary action."

I developed a strong committee of medical directors from major corporations in the United States, and from the Bell Telephone Company in Canada. Each year we made certain that we had an interesting and newsworthy program for our audience, and we received good publicity year after year wherever the annual meeting was held. This publicity led to a succession of spin-off situations for me, such as being invited as guest speaker at the annual meetings of other associations.

In 1950 the American Association of Life Insurance Medical Directors met in Waterloo, Ontario. As guest speaker, I had the opportunity to address another influential group of physicians, trying to persuade them to adopt a more enlightened approach to insuring alcohol addicts who were recovering. Up to that time "uncontrolled drinkers" (in the eyes of the insurance companies) usually found it impossible to obtain life insurance, in spite of their varying periods of sobriety.

I don't know if any of the companies modified their policies because of my beliefs, but at least I had the chance to persuade these influential people to think about the possibility of recovery from addiction. I also wanted them to realize that recovery was a long-term process, and that it was an endeavor which warranted endorsement and support from all significant groups in the community, including the life-insurance industry. My address to the medical directors of the life-insurance industry was also indicative, I believe, of the slowly growing interest in problem drinking as a social issue in Canada.

CHAPTER SEVEN

The Willowdale Hospital

After closing Glenmaple in 1947 we continued to receive requests to treat female patients. Since Shadow Brook was licensed to treat only males, we were forced to turn women away or to try to treat them in their own homes. I found this situation very disturbing, because unlike their male counterparts, female alcoholics could find help only in regular hospitals for specific medical ailments, like cirrhosis. I firmly believed that the best treatment they could receive would be in an appropriate clinical setting.

Our first patient at Glenmaple exemplified the problem we were now facing. A few years after her initial treatment, we received a call from the woman's family. She had apparently fallen off the wagon again, much to the anguish of her husband and children, and they were unable to cope with the situation in their chaotic household. My wife and I wholeheartedly agreed that I should not venture into their home by myself, so we both went out on the call. Mary always accompanied me when I was forced to pay a visit to a home where there was an intoxicated female. Mary was usually a calming influence on them, as well as a witness and an assistant if necessary.

Our former patient had just won a war of wits with her family. Her husband and sons had held a council of war and had decided that she was going to sober up, whether she liked it or not. They reasoned that if there was no liquor in the house and if she remained at home, she would eventually sober up. They very carefully searched the house from top to bottom, and everything containing alcohol, including vanilla extract, perfume, mouthwash, and cough medicine, was thrown out. Yet for a while, they had been unable to discover why the woman remained pleasantly high day after day.

One of the boys finally began to catch on. His mother had continued to prepare all their meals, in spite of her rather wobbly condition. Since she had never welcomed her family's intrusion into her kitchen, the family had respected her territorial claims. Suspecting that the kitchen held the key to her inebriation the son waited until she was safely away from her domain one day and made a quick check of the area. As he had suspected, he found the gallon jar for white vinegar half full of gin and the one for dark vinegar half full of rye. Because the family had made the mistake of threatening to search the house and cut off her supplies long before they acted, the woman had had plenty of time to replenish and hide her stock. When they realized how thoroughly they had been outmaneuvered, they threw in the towel and told her to drink as much as she wished. Then they called us.

Mary and I spent several hours with the woman, but left without being able to convince her to accept any kind of advice or help. I was quite upset by the knowledge that home-care just wouldn't work in such cases. Our former patient eventually won control over her addiction for a year or so with the renewed help of AA, but she later relapsed and died from an overdose of sedatives. Her tragic example highlighted the need for a clinical setting for treating women with addiction problems as we did for men.

Since we were still paying off debts from the Glenmaple venture, we hesitated to go further into debt, even though we were receiving requests to open a clinic for women. In the end, the reasons for establishing such a facility far outweighed the economic rationale for avoiding the project. The years between 1948 and 1951 had been particularly difficult for us, and we felt that we had no real choice.

On the basis of our Glenmaple experience, I estimated that the ratio of male to female alcoholics requesting treatment was about four to one. Mary and I were soon once again touring the countryside looking for a suitable location, and eventually found a small brick house in our own Toronto suburb, Willowdale, which was within walking distance of our home. Again it became necessary for us to meet with the neighbors and reassure them about our patients before the township would amend the zoning bylaw to allow us to proceed. I had already become convinced that a hospital, rather than a sanitarium license, would best serve our purpose. People were "committed" to sanitariums, sometimes against their will. The certification of all patients at Shadow Brook had become a nuisance, and we did not intend to hold any patients against their will anyway. We knew we could get a hospital license; all we needed was the money to proceed with the operation.

The Shadow Brook patients were quite interested in the proposed new facility for women, and one of them introduced me to a man who loaned us enough money to purchase the property and equip a small hospital. As partial protection on his investment this man took back a second mortgage at a moderate rate of interest. He was a rather stern, quiet man in his early sixties. He listened carefully, spoke tersely, and revealed little about himself until our last meeting, which was years later. On that occasion, when we were delivering a payment on the loan, he asked, "How much do you still owe?" When I told him about a thousand dollars he smiled, thought for a moment, and then said, "You've paid enough." He called in his secretary and asked her to prepare a discharge of mortgage and a confirmation that the debt had been paid in full. I was stunned. We had become so accustomed to living with loans, mortgages, and debts that it was difficult to believe that we had actually received a gift of this kind.

In keeping with our policy of naming our clinics after the area or natural setting, the new women's clinic was called Willowdale Hospital. By this time the officials at the Ministry of Health were becoming accustomed to having me drop in. They appreciated all the reasons for my request to open the Willowdale facility, and they agreed to grant me a license to operate a seven-bed hospital (three single rooms and two doubles). Of course, we could not open the clinic without a few additional problems. At Willowdale we ran into the unexpected expense of having to fireproof the old house according to municipal and provincial specifications. I kept learning about the problems of dealing with government agencies when I discovered that the specifications changed with each jurisdiction.

While all these preparations were going on there was evidence emerging of society's new interest in the problems of addiction. The Addiction Research Foundation, which was founded in 1949 by the Ontario government with a mandate to conduct research, began to explore all aspects of alcohol abuse. One or two new private addiction clinics opened up in the early 1950s and the Salvation Army expanded its work with skid-row alcoholics. I watched these new developments with interest, and in 1953 became involved as a consultant with a Salvation Army project called Harbour Light.

Brigadier Joshua Monk of the Salvation Army in Toronto ran a small facility called Harbour Light on Queen Street. He eventually acquired a larger location at the corner of Jarvis and Shuter (where the operation still exists), to provide homeless alcoholics with daily needs and to help them overcome their addiction. In 1960 I agreed to spend some time each Saturday morning with the director of the program and the alcoholics themselves. I hoped to share experiences and treatment techniques with them, and perhaps make use of what I was learning about these alcoholics at a reformatory clinic with which I had become involved. Unfortunately, in 1963 I was forced to give up my involvement with Harbour Light. However, I continued to follow the endeavors of the Salvation Army and to support its efforts to help those unfortunate people who have wound up on skid row.

Willowdale Hospital had three directors — Mary and I and our old faithful friend, Mac, who was always obliging and usually sober. I don't think there was a connection, but Mac joined AA shortly after we opened Willowdale, where he found a new meaning to life, permanent sobriety, and adequate compensation for giving up the old. He believed that there was a good market for our unique service for women, and that our primary initial task should be to keep down expenses. We were in complete agreement with our budget-conscious co-director, but there were basic costs that we could not reduce. For example, we had to have nurses on duty at all times, and we looked for people who were prepared to assume a wide variety of responsibilities.

Like their counterparts at Shadow Brook, our Willowdale nurses not only carried out the combined roles of nurses and interns, but also did daily posting, assumed administrative responsibilities, collected accounts, and pitched in as cooks, housekeepers, and family counselors when necessary. The were also trained to share in the total management and planning of the clinic. Mary Epp supervised the new nursing staff when she was off-duty from Shadow Brook. She took on added responsibilities willingly, even though her life was just as hectic as ours. My wife Mary served as secretary-treasurer and business manager in addition to all the other administrative and household details she had to manage. The only time her enthusiasm for the new venture waned was when she had to use part of my paycheck from Shadow Brook to cover part of the Willowdale payroll.

In order to cope with her new responsibilities, Mary

arranged for a succession of unmarried girls in varying stages of pregnancy to live with us and take care of our four children. The referring agency had arranged that prenatal care and delivery be carried out at St. Michael's Hospital in Toronto, where our own children had been born. Without exception, each girl went into labor between midnight and dawn, which forced me into headlong dashes for downtown Toronto at those unearthly hours. My embarrassment increased with each trip, as I repeatedly faced the soon-familiar faces of the nuns at the admissions desk, although they never asked any pointed questions. I almost wished they would so that I could explain my regular reappearance there with a different pregnant girl every few months. I settled for putting on my best professional manner and acting the part of a busy physician who had to rush through this routine task in order to get on with more important matters. The nuns' expressions implied alert efficiency but completely masked everything else.

The Shadow Brook staff of physicians and psychologists worked with the female patients on a fee-for-service basis when they were not engaged elsewhere. An attempt was made to approximate the group counseling and follow-up procedures being explored at Shadow Brook, but this turned out to be difficult: as was the case at Glenmaple, the group was too small. Also, the women seemed only slightly enthusiastic about such a program. Many had to be pushed to tidy themselves up, get out of their dressing-gowns, and get dressed every morning. Interestingly enough, this had not been a problem at Glenmaple, where we had had patients of both sexes. We observed that this attitude disappeared when we opened up the Bell Clinic for both men and women a few years later.

When we opened Willowdale Hospital in November 1951, social attitudes toward female alcoholics were even less tolerant than they were toward men. I soon began to suspect why. Most of the women were in more serious trouble than the men. For the most part, our female patients came from middle- and upper-class families, had never had to get up each morning and go to work, and on the whole presented a history of more continuous drinking than did the men, who were forced to curtail their habit during business hours.

There were many other reasons why women would show up at our clinic in such bad shape. These patients also suffered from malnutrition more often than the men did. Combined with chronic intoxication, this often resulted in advanced damage to their livers and nervous systems. These women often harbored greater feelings of shame and rejection by their families, on top of facing a lack of treatment facilities for them and their special problems. Our staff and consultants were often startled by their poor physical condition. Organic brain damage was common, and their average mood was one of "agitated depression." Our female patients soon taught us just how severe the withdrawal reactions to alcohol could be, and they stimulated our search for a means of reducing or preventing the more serious manifestations of convulsions and delirium.

Although our experiences at Shadow Brook and Willowdale gradually reassured us of our ability to cope with most acute conditions, there were a few patients each year who were so unmanageable that they could only be transferred to one of the provincial hospitals or to the Homewood Sanitarium in Guelph, Ontario. In most cases we were able to sedate our patients with bug juice, although it was unequal to the tasks of controlling the D.T.s. Some of our more delirious patients became even more unmanageable when treated with barbiturates, so paraldehyde remained for us the one reasonably reliable medication. But other patients required something more. Why was it, for example, that some hallucinating patients became confused, disoriented, and delirious and others did not?

I knew that heavy drinkers were prone to develop the D.T.s following an operation or injury, and that this was frequently a serious problem for the surgical staffs of the larger hospitals. There were occasional references in the medical literature to the possibility that malnutrition contributed to the severity of alcohol withdrawal. One surgeon in New York claimed to have reduced the incidence of D.T.s before an operation by giving his heavy-drinking patients an intravenous infusion of the essential amino acids, the key building blocks that combine to form protein.

Assuming that all of our patients suffered from some degree of malnutrition, I began to look for a protein supplement to be used routinely along with our vitamins. There were a few on the market at that time, but most of them were so unpalatable that I had little hope of persuading patients to continue taking them long enough to do any good. Finally I discovered a product called Provimalt, which had an acceptable taste and contained all the ingredients I sought, but was the devil's own to mix. We encouraged all our patients, with the exception of those with gross liver disease, to drink as much Provimalt as they could tolerate during the first few days following admission. Although there was no way to prove that it worked, the medical and nursing staff were of the impression that there was a significant decrease in the frequency and severity of delirium tremens in patients following their Provimalt consumption.

We had the singular good fortune during our early years to have the support of two outstanding consultants in internal medicine — Dr. William Hall, then of St. Michael's Hospital and the late Dr. Jean Davey of Women's College Hospital. They gave us access to two general hospitals for patients too ill to be cared for with our limited resources. I also arranged for an old friend and classmate, Dr. Ricky Schachter, to act as our consultant in dermatology, since many of our patients had a wide variety of skin disorders requiring special care. It was becoming increasingly evident that the patients we received at Willowdale and Shadow Brook might have various combinations of physical as well as mental and social problems, which could require some type of continuing care for long periods of time. All in all, we felt reasonably pleased with our efforts in dealing with drinkers of both sexes, but we looked forward to the day when we could house all our addiction patients under one roof.

CHAPTER EIGHT

The Alex G. Brown Clinic

Prior to 1950, the majority of alcoholics on skid row were summarily dealt with on a light punitive basis, which meant that they were sentenced to a regional reformatory for three months at a time. There were about six reformatories throughout the province. Mimico Reformatory, closest to Toronto, had the largest regular alcoholic population. In the late 1940s and early 1950s Alex G. Brown was superintendent of the Mimico Reformatory, which was operated by the Department of Reform Institutions. Situated a few miles west of downtown Toronto, the reformatory usually accommodated about 400 "guests" from the Toronto area, most of whom were there for the same reason: breach of the Liquor Control Act (BLCA), the most common "crime" in the province.

Alex was an enthusiastic participant in any plan to improve the well-being of his flock. Along with Frank Potts, chief psychologist for the department, they were determined to do something about the "revolving door" problem at Mimico. Frank returned from the Yale Summer School of Alcoholic Studies in 1950 with fresh ideas, and he received strong support from the minister of the department, John Foote, a former clergyman turned politician and a recipient of the Victoria Cross for his bravery at Dieppe. So, with both grass-roots and executive support, plans were developed with surprising speed.

A large brick mansion that had formerly served as a home for delinquent boys was restored and refurnished to accommodate thirty-two patients. I first learned of these plans in the spring of 1951 when I received an invitation to see Foote, at his office in the legislative buildings in Toronto. He asked if I would act as a consultant to the department and assume responsibility for organizing the treatment and rehabilitation program for their new clinic. I would be dealing with patients who had been brought there from all over the province.

I agreed at once, without a thought about where I would find the time. Shadow Brook was busy with its male patients, and plans were well advanced for the new Willowdale Hospital for women. I was still responsible for the health services of Christie Brown & Company, Highland Dairy, A. Kimball, and Noxzema, and was in my first year as chairman of the Committee on Problem Drinking for the American Association of Industrial Physicians and Surgeons. Upon learning that I could retain this position without having to remain active in industrial-health work, I reluctantly cut myself adrift from the four small companies I had served for five years.

Tragedy struck a few weeks before the clinic was to open. Alex Brown, the man who had worked so hard for the facility and who had earned the respect of the prisoners and everyone else who knew him, died suddenly of a heart attack. John Foote promptly recommended that the clinic be named after him, and in September 1951 the Alex G. Brown Memorial Clinic officially opened. Alex's widow became the office manager, and her warmth and understanding contributed immeasurably to the welcoming atmosphere we wished to create.

In looking for the counseling and follow-up staff, the clinic examined the work records of the guards and custodial staff, many of whom were already trusted and respected by the inmates. They had been on the job long enough to have no illusions about the problems alcoholics faced. They also knew what the prisoners did "on the outside" — where they hung out and with whom, their family backgrounds, their records, and most importantly, the attitude of the police toward drunks. Accordingly, I came to instruct a very capable, dedicated group of men in the techniques we used at Shadow Brook.

Some of the Mimico regulars had been charged with the usual three-month BLCA sentence several times a year for up to twenty or thirty years. The new plan was to offer inmates with drinking offenses the opportunity to volunteer for treatment in the new Mimico clinic during the last month of their sentence. As soon as their supervising staffs had been oriented to the design and purpose of our new clinic, the option was extended to inmates of all reformatories in the province. Applicants were screened by the administration staff, and only those considered serious about making a new life for themselves were accepted. Although the criteria for selection were inexact, inconsistent, and based mainly on personal impressions from actual contact with the prisoners, I was satisfied with the carefully considered opinion of those with whom I worked on the selection committee.

I did not have to worry about treating intoxication or the D.T.s, since this group of patients at the Alex G. Brown Clinic had been dry for at least two months. A capable male nurse was instructed in how to use Antabuse properly, and educated in the need for protein and vitamin supplements. All of the staff sat in on my weekly lectures and discussions with the patients. It was encouraging to find that I was accepted by this new patient group and that they seemed to understand what I was talking about. From their feedback I was exposed to many clinical and social situations that were entirely new to me. The staff quickly picked up our concept of total health. They became increasingly proficient in giving talks and leading the discussions and they also became adept at using and explaining the films we had incorporated into the second phase of the Shadow Brook plan.

In addition to continuing contact with their rehabilitation officers, the "graduates" of the Alex G. Brown Clinic met weekly in Trinity Church in Toronto. The rehab. officers put in hours and hours of overtime without receiving any additional pay, which strengthened my conviction that a genuine desire to serve was a more important qualification than a professional degree in the clinical management of addiction. So many addicts lose faith in themselves and their fellows. An essential part of their recovery is a restoration of that faith, and this requires the help of dedicated workers. No amount of academic training will help if the desire is not there.

I found it important to stress the statement by William James, the famous nineteenth-century American psychologist and philosopher, that people rarely live to the limit of their abilities, and that they possess powers that they habitually fail to use. By emphasizing this belief, together with a total health approach within a caring community setting, I believed that patients enjoyed the best medium for developing and fulfilling their latent abilities.

I began their treatment by telling the chronically drunk offenders that if they wished to be guests here forever, that was their business. If not, they would have to pay close attention to me. I told them that they had important reservoirs of unused abilities, and that when combined with those of the staff, their friends, their families, and their associates, this currently unused power could provide them with a strong new start in life. "What do you have to lose? Why not give it a go?" I suggested. I didn't have to keep reminding them that their lives were out of control; they knew that already. They also knew that the only way to survive and develop a new life was to learn how to stop drinking for good.

Many jumped at the chance to try the extra help offered by Antabuse. One man in his late forties had been incarcerated repeatedly for many years. He was unusual for that patient group in that he had also acquired cirrhosis of the liver and had been treated in St. Michael's Hospital. The man said that he wanted to try to do something different with his life and wanted to take Antabuse. At that time we avoided giving Antabuse to anyone who had a history of liver disease. When I explained this to him, he was very disappointed. I arranged for him to have special medication, but I asked him to keep it to himself and I gave him a year's supply to take when he left. I also gave him strict instructions not to drink while he was taking this medicine. He promised faithfully that he would follow my instructions and he left with a year's supply of lactose (milk sugar) tablets that he was to take once daily.

About a year later I had a call from a man who identified himself as the brother of the man I had put on the daily lactose medication. "I just wanted to tell you how delighted we are," he said. "My brother was truly the black sheep of the family. We had had little contact with him for many years and when he came out of the Alex G. Brown Clinic about a year ago he seemed to be a different person. He started looking for a job, particularly one that nobody else would want. He decided on cleaning chimneys and fireplaces and eventually got himself the most rickety old truck you can imagine. Now he's in business for himself, appears to be quite happy rattling around cleaning chimneys, and he hasn't had a drink for over a year." To me his story was additional proof of the wisdom of William James.

The Alex G. Brown Clinic gave me other opportunities to meet men whose lives were intriguing. "Jim" was in his sixties, and according to one of the members of the screening committee, had been around longer than the deputy minister. His first arrest for drunkenness had been about thirty years earlier, and he had spent most of the productive years of his life in the reformatory. I recall trying to estimate the cost of Jim's alcohol problem to the province — the work hours involved in his arrest and trial, the cost of his years of incarceration, and the loss of productivity for such a long period of time — but I gave up when I realized that the costs of setting up treatment services were negligible compared with the ever-expanding costs to the individual and society of an uncontrolled dependency on alcohol and/or drugs.

To the surprise of everyone who knew him, Jim applied for treatment at the new clinic. The first reaction of the screening committee was to turn him down. They believed that there were many others more likely to benefit from our plan. As the only member of the committee to see him for the first time, however, I was intrigued. He impressed me as a man who felt almost totally defeated by life — but not quite. I thought that I detected a desperate sincerity in his request for help in living his last years out of jail. The rest of the committee politely acquiesced in my recommendation, and Jim was allowed in.

Having assumed responsibility for his admission, I followed Jim's progress with special interest. He was cooperative and seemed interested in the program during his month in the clinic, although I thought that much of the orientation course was unnecessary for him. Like others, he did not need to be convinced of his need to stop drinking. For him, the main advantage of the lectures, films, and discussion was that they provided a new emotional experience. Like a great many others there, his ability to absorb instruction had been dulled by recurrent intoxication, age, and disuse of his mind in an understimulating environment. The lectures and other group activities brought staff and patients together and, although harmony was far from universal and communication difficult, the fact that the project was new and held out hope was as exciting to him as it was to the others.

After his stay at the clinic, Jim ventured forth courageously into what was for him a frightening world, with the protection of both Antabuse and a man named Don Griggs. Griggs was a dedicated, understanding rehabilitation officer, whose past experience as a policeman provided him with an excellent basis for appreciating Jim's problems.

But Jim required more than Antabuse and a rehabilitation officer. He had not had any dental care for years and what teeth he retained were in appalling condition. There was no doubt in my mind that Jim would feel a lot better about himself with a new set of "choppers." I called an old friend, Jack Macdonald, who was at that time a member of the faculty of dentistry at the University of Toronto, and still carrying on a part-time practice. I told Jack that he was about to acquire a new patient who required some dental surgery and a complete set of dentures, and that I wanted him to provide this little service free of charge. As expected, this elicited some choice profanities from Jack, but also as expected he entered fully into the spirit of the project. Jim's new teeth did wonders for both his appearance and his spirits.

Don Griggs got him a job at the posh National Club in downtown Toronto and Jim showed up for work complete with a new suit of clothes and the dentures. It was a very respectable place and it was certainly not dry, but Griggs felt that Jim should take the risk because jobs were hard to find for anyone his age. He did well, and though he often felt lonely living away from his old friends on skid row, his motivation remained and he took pride in his new situation. He would often go down to the courtrooms on his days off and watch some of his old buddies passing through on their weary merry-go-round through the justice system.

But we also had our failures and disappointments which we reluctantly learned to accept as inevitable. The one that impressed me as approaching the ultimate human tragedy was "Bill," who was fifty-one when I first met him. Bill was born in Northern Ireland. His mother died in childbirth and for the first two years of his life he was cared for by his maternal grandmother because his father was in South Africa fighting in the Boer War. Bill's father remarried soon after his return from Africa and took his son home. From that time on, Bill's life was a continuous hell. I gained the impression that Bill's mother and grandmother had come from a refined, learned family, but that his handsome father had come from a very different background. Bill's father apparently was a boisterous, uncouth, and cruel man, and his second marriage had been to a woman much like himself. His grandmother, who appreciated the boy's unusual intelligence and aptitude, was rarely permitted to see him.

When a stepsister was born, everything worsened for him. He usually came first in his classes at school, which evoked no reaction whatsoever at home; but when he came second he was beaten, and often starved. He was so frequently punished in this way that he often fainted when on parade with the school cadets. Bill had always been very interested in music, but when a piano was bought for his sister (who never did learn to play it), the lid was slammed down on his fingers if he touched the keys. It was clear that he was an unwanted child.

The family left Northern Ireland in 1912 and moved to Winnipeg, where Bill's father got work in the freight yards. By this time his stepmother was seriously addicted to alcohol. The move to Canada had disturbed her routines for maintaining a supply, and Bill was assigned a new role as her runner. In return for his regular trips to the bootlegger and for not telling his father, his mother rewarded him with a slug from the bottle. Since this was the first act of kindness he could remember, he welcomed the booze, and he soon came to enjoy the warm, glowing feeling it gave him. He never experienced any unpleasant reactions or side-effects.

As Bill entered his teens, he developed into a thin, gangly youth with knobby joints, big hands and feet, and a shy, self-conscious manner. His father lost no opportunity to ridicule his son not only about his appearance but also about his knowledge. Despite this ridicule, Bill continued to do exceptionally well at school and had come to know a clergyman, who like his grandmother, recognized his unusual capabilities. The clergyman went to Bill's father and asked if he would let him arrange to have Bill finish high school and then go on to university. This only made matters at home worse. His father forced Bill to quit school as soon as the law allowed, and got him a job at the freight yards instead. But Bill's photographic memory for car numbers and schedules soon made him more effective at the job than his father, and the relationship between the two deteriorated even further.

During this time Bill's dependence on alcohol was increasing. He relied on it for the only pleasant feelings he had, and he began to obtain a supply for his own use. He was too shy to make friends, and for about fifteen years — until 1929 — he lived at home and worked for the railroad. When he finally did make a break, he went to Chicago to train for a job with the elevated railway. But soon after his arrival there came the stock market crash of 1929, and there was no work to be had. He drifted to Toronto, where he met a woman who soon became the most important person in his life. She loved him in spite of the alcohol problem that was beginning to take control of him. Since he was always broke, he was occasionally arrested for vagrancy, but she was always waiting for him when he got out of the reformatory. In spite of the bitter opposition of her family for taking up with a "drunken bum," they were married and a son was born in 1936. Bill could not get over the wonder of having a wife and child, but by then his addiction so completely controlled him that he had little chance to be with them.

When his wife's health began to fail, she and the child were taken into her sister's home on the condition that Bill would not be allowed to see them again — under any circumstances.

When Bill was able to remain sober he could usually get part-time work, because he was a jack-of-all-trades. And even when he fell off the wagon, his unusual memory and knowledge of many subjects earned him special recognition among his drinking buddies. They referred to him as "The Mayor of Skid Row."

Bill came to the Alex G. Brown Clinic in the late fall of 1951, a broken man. On his previous release from a three-month stretch at the Mimico Reformatory he had telephoned his wife, but had not been able to speak with her. Her sister told him that she had a cold and was in bed. About a week later he found out that she had been dying of pneumonia when he had been trying to reach her and she had been buried three days before.

The rehabilitation officers would sometimes phone me for advice in dealing with one of their flock when he slipped from grace. They tried hard to interrupt a relapse in its early stages to avoid having their patients picked up by the police and processed through the courts again. Unfortunately, there was no way for the Alex G. Brown Clinic to establish a consistent service, since it could treat only those who were already in the department's custody. They had no budget to cover the expenses of outside care, and patients like Bill usually had no money.

Since the Bell family was already accustomed to having patients in the house, a few weeks after Bill had completed his month at the clinic we took him in. At that time we had four children under the age of ten and the oldest three, Ronald, Janice, and Linda constantly vied for the privilege of playing nurse. Our youngest daughter, Mary, who was then eighteen months old, was quick and alert, and was also an inquisitive, friendly sprite. She quickly formed a strong attachment to Bill, whose proudest moment came when she refused to allow anybody else to put her snowsuit on her. I remember coming home one winter's day just as they were leaving for a walk, hand-in-hand, the shambling broken man and the lively little girl.

Before Don Griggs could figure out what to do with Bill on a long-term basis, we had an urgent request to help another man who was in imminent danger of being arrested. I called Jack Macdonald and suggested that since he also had a spare room he should take Bill and we would take the new patient. I suggested that Bill could do many of those odd jobs that neither of us ever managed to get done, and Jack agreed. Before Bill moved to Jack Macdonald's house, however, he told me his life story during interviews we often conducted into the small hours of the morning. From time to time he displayed flashes of the abilities that had impressed his grandmother, the clergyman in Winnipeg, the gentle woman who had loved and married him, and his skid-row friends. But for the most part he seemed utterly defeated by life, and too tired and apathetic to try over again. In spite of his latent potential, Bill had lacked the toughness and resiliency to cope with his family difficulties throughout his teens and twenties. As he grew older, his life merely shifted to come under the equally effective control of an addiction. He had rarely enjoyed the sense of fulfillment that comes with personal success.

Not long after he moved in, Bill got into Jack's scotch. Jack told me in terse, forceful terms that there was a limit to how far he was willing to go to accommodate my unusual client. He promptly stretched that limit by allowing Bill to stay with him. In April, Mary and I left for the annual meeting of the American Association of Industrial Physicians and Surgeons. Because of our hectic schedules, Jack and I were unable to discuss Bill before I left. This was unfortunate; he was fairly certain that Bill was nibbling again. When Bill tried to stop on his own and began hallucinating, Jack had the dubious distinction of being the only dentist I knew to have undertaken the treatment of the D.T.s single-handed. But his skill in injecting local anesthetics stood him in good stead and he administered copious quantities of B-complex vitamins to Bill, wisely avoided sedation, and planned dire vengeance upon me on my return.

Soon after he recovered from this episode, Bill had a new home and a job, thanks again mainly to the efforts of Don Griggs. He remained sober, got some new clothes, and even began to exhibit a little more hope and pride in himself. His greatest wish remained that he might eventually be able to see his son now and again, but every effort he made to contact the boy was blocked by his in-laws.

Don Griggs told me the final chapter in Bill's tragic story. He was on the street one day, completely sober, well dressed, with money in his pocket, when he met his son. They happened to meet in front of a sporting-goods store, and Bill asked the boy if there was anything there he liked. Glad to see his father again, the boy picked out something and they went into the store to buy it. But as they came back out onto the street, Bill ran into his sister-in-law. She created a terrible scene, screamed at her nephew to give back the present, and warned him never to speak to "that drunken bum" of a father again.

That episode finished Bill. He resumed his heavy drinking, showed no desire ever again to quit, and died later that year. He was fifty-two years old.

Although I was unable to undertake scientifically controlled studies, I did learn about differences between the two groups of patients at Shadow Brook and at the Alex G. Brown Clinic. The Brown group tended to be less defensive and secretive, because the men had nothing more to lose. They were not motivated to stay sober as an alternative to being fired, jailed, or separated from their families, because the latter had already happened to them. On the other hand, they seemed to be unusually honest, if for no other reason than that there was nothing for them to gain in the clinic by lying. They could easily spot a phony or a do-gooder, and it was necessary for us to prove ourselves sincere to each group of patients before they would begin to share their experiences and ideas and listen to any suggestions from us.

We also had to be prepared for unusual questions at the Alex G. Brown Clinic. A patient in his mid-forties asked to see me privately toward the end of his month there. He was a thin, dark, tense person who looked me straight in the eye for a few seconds, then abruptly asked, "Doctor, do you believe in God, and if so, why?"

Since I had expected a more immediately relevant question about Antabuse or vitamins, I could not have been more surprised if the man had pulled a gun. From the expression on his face, I saw that he was deadly serious, and that it was important that my reply be equally so. The fact that I struggled so hard to express my barely crystallized beliefs must have satisfied him, because he went on to explain some of the other thoughts that led to his question. Was I on the level? Was I just trying to make a big name for myself, and use the inmates as guinea pigs? Did I really believe that a life without alcohol could be possible, and that it could be maintained because it was preferable? Did I really believe that people possessed far greater abilities than they ever used, which was one reason why past failure did not necessarily mean future failure? Before the interview had ended I had begun to suspect that he was asking these questions on behalf of the whole group and that it represented the culmination of hours of discussion following my lectures.

Many of the Brown patients were far from impressed with the prospects we were offering them for the future. One patient expressed his feelings quite clearly in a group discussion: "If I go along with your suggestion and stay sober, get a room away from the old district, and get a job, I'll have about as much money as I do now — nothing! After I pay for my room, meals, clothes, and tobacco, my check will be gone, and besides, I'll be lonely. There's got to be more than mere survival, because I've already got that. I don't have to work any harder in the reformatory than I would outside, and the only friends I have left are right here. Why should I bother?"

I had some difficulty answering him, and admitted that there was little advantage to pursuing a program unless he wished to take a chance on finding rewards from pursuing new and healthier goals. Although I believed this, I had misgivings about its application for many of the

Brown patients. I wondered why it was necessary to acquire a criminal record in order to find a suitably protective environment. The inmates of the reformatory and the Alex G. Brown Clinic reminded me of soldiers who gripe about their lot in the army, but who actually prefer to have their lives determined by others. Many old soldiers show their greatest anxiety not in battle but at the prospect of being discharged. Some men probably regarded discharge from the reformatory as similar to a weekend spree during military service. They counted on the police to bring them back to the "barracks" and security before they could do too much harm outside.

After explaining the meaning of blackouts, the shakes, hallucinations, and other conditions associated with alcohol and drug addiction, I would ask the patient groups at Shadow Brook and the Brown Clinic to indicate by a show of hands if they had experienced the various symptoms, and at what age. The responses from the two groups were quite different. The Brown Clinic patients experienced blackouts more consistently and at an earlier age. This effect of intoxication was recognized by the patient as an inability to remember, but was considered by others to be a gross disturbance in their behavior. This dramatic change in behavior was a recurring and consistent feature of the problem with many of these patients, and it undoubtedly contributed to their frequent arrests. The Shadow Brook patients, on the other hand, tended to report blackouts at a later age, and some of them had never experienced the phenomenon at all. Many Shadow Brook patients had damaged livers, while few of the Brown group reported treatment for liver disease. On the other hand, both Shadow Brook and Brown patients spoke of "pins and needles," tingling and burning of the feet and hands, both of which are indicative of malnutrition from vitamin-B deficiency.

In those days I regarded liver disease as another manifestation of malnutrition, and I was puzzled by indications of damage to one part of the body, but not to others. I considered the possibility that a patient could have liver disease without knowing it, since the symptoms could be vague or absent and very few of the men had regular medical examinations. However, the examinations of patients on admission to the Brown Clinic rarely revealed serious liver damage. I concluded that the holiday from heavy drinking enforced by the Department of Reform Institutions was sparing the livers of the Brown group from the damage of executive-type bottle-a-day drinking.

The two groups of patients also had different socioeconomic backgrounds and showed different degrees of deterioration in their family, work, and community relationships. The Shadow Brook group was much more defensive but generally more intelligent and better educated. This latter asset was often counterbalanced by the fact that their mental faculties had so recently been dulled by the effects of prolonged semi-anesthesia. Physically, the Brown group seemed to be more influenced by recurrent acute intoxication, and the Shadow Brook patients by chronic changes. Both groups reported a comparable incidence of the shakes, hallucinations, convulsions and the D.T.s. The common and most impressive factor with both groups was the power of addiction — its ability to control the strong as well as the weak, in spite of the individual's awareness of the danger, insights into its nature, and a genuine desire to escape from its frightening embrace.

My involvement with the Alex G. Brown Clinic ended in the early 1960s. The program was running well, and I had to allocate whatever time I had to the development of the new Donwood Institute. The Brown Clinic experience had given me valuable insights into the problems of addiction among the indigent and the complex difficulties in their clinical and social management. In October 1973, the Brown Clinic was incorporated into the general program of the Ontario Correctional Institute in Brampton.

CHAPTER NINE

A Rocky Road to Recovery

Our experiences at Shadow Brook from 1948 to 1954 were making us increasingly aware of the tragic reality of addiction to alcohol and sedative drugs, and of the need to improve our methods and facilities. We were losing far too many truly talented individuals; the obituary columns reminded us constantly of the price of failure. In spite of our apparent successes with numerous patients, we completely failed with many others. I can remember some of them so clearly: brilliant, charming, artistic, often lonely people who died in degrading and horrible ways. There was the physician who burned to death in a flophouse, the writer who died in convulsions, the business executive who committed suicide by deliberately smashing his car into a railway abutment, and so many others.

This nagging sense of impotence was one of the reasons that I was so impressed with the AA program, which saved many other talented people from a similar fate. Throughout the forties, fifties, and sixties I attended AA meetings frequently, not only to better understand the program and philosophy of the organization, but also to consider how a clinical program could supplement their objectives. As a result I was often invited to address the members, and Mary and I always received a warm welcome. In fact, she told me that if anything ever happened to me and she felt lonely, she would go to an AA meeting where she knew she would be welcomed. This, in spite of the fact that she had no addictions to alcohol or drugs.

During my clinical years I had learned to pay special attention to three conditions that were regarded as routine hazards to our patients, particularly during the first year of recovery. They were tension, fatigue, and loneliness, any one of which could drive a patient back to his or her addiction. In the early days of Shadow Brook I had assumed that I understood the causes of tension fairly well — reactions to current crises, to nervous-system stimulants, extended tension states dating from childhood, swings in mood, and the like. But certain patients began to experience states of tension that did not seem to come under any of these categories. I was intrigued by the comments of wives that they could always tell when "the old man was getting ready for a bout." They described recurrent states of tension, restlessness, and irritability that did not appear to be reactions to current problems. Nonetheless, I could not rule out the possibility of some form of chronic tension building up gradually to the breaking-point in these patients.

There seemed to be a connection between this phenomenon and the term "dry drunks," which I heard many times in AA circles. The term had a number of meanings for those who used it, none of which appeared to be related to anything in the medical literature. Fortunately, the continuing-therapy program at Shadow Brook had given us the opportunity to observe some of our patients for several consecutive years. I gradually realized that by the end of the second year most patients recovering from their addiction were free of many of the problems and tensions that had threatened their sobriety during their first year.

An alert, intelligent business executive was in his first year of recovery from both alcohol and barbiturate drug addiction following treatment at Shadow Brook. Much of the time he was tense, angry, and obviously experiencing serious physical and emotional distress, but he had not relapsed. After exhaustive questioning I felt that there were no current problems to explain so serious a state of stress. I doubted the possibility of any underlying psychiatric disability. I was extremely reluctant to try alleviating his discomfort with any kind of nervous-system depressant, because of his history of barbiturate addiction. (This was during the pre-tranquilizer era, and the choice of drugs was limited.) I had almost decided that my safest course would be to use the old bug juice when the man lost patience with me and my curious probing.

"Goddammit, Doctor!" he shouted finally, "stop fooling around and do something! Can't you see I'm desperate? I might have been better off getting drunk on my own if this is all you're going to do! Can't you see that I feel just like I do when I'm coming off a bout? But this time I haven't *had* anything!"

The work of several American physicians had piqued my curiosity in the possibility of a functional disturbance of the pituitary and adrenal glands, caused by the prolonged effect of high concentrations of alcohol in the body. For this reason we had available a supply of adrenocortical extract (ACE), but we had not found occasion to use it up to that time. When we finally found a vein in this man that had not been sclerosed from previous injections of sodium amytal, we gave our first intravenous treatment with adrenocortical extract. The positive result was dramatic — for both of us. A second injection that day and two more the next completed the treatment, and the man left for Chicago to address a convention of business associates the following day. This patient recovered completely from his dependence on alcohol and barbiturates.

Let me explain here what I believe to be the difference between "recovered" and "recovering." I have always considered patients to be recovered if they are no longer constantly thinking about and desiring the substance to which they have been addicted. They are no longer concentrating on other daily activities in order to avoid succumbing again to their addiction. By this time, too, the physiological imbalances affecting them when they were addicted have been corrected. People are still recovering, however, when they are still *aware* that they are not drinking or taking drugs. They are still concentrating on controlling any desires to resume their habits. This recovering period will vary with each patient, the substance being abused, and the intensity of that abuse. (I can say from personal experience that I suffered from unpleasant dreams for quite a few years after finally quitting cigarettes for good. In those dreams I was always resuming my old smoking pattern and hating myself for it. It wasn't until the dreams finally ended that I knew I was "recovered.") Of course, the addiction can reactivate during either the recovering or the recovered phases. There are no guarantees of a permanent recovery in the addiction field.

We continued to use the ACE treatment for emergencies of tension, and occasionally to treat patients in the acute phase of withdrawal. But it was rarely so dramatically effective as it had been on our first patient, and sometimes it seemed to have no effect at all. It was also too expensive to be used routinely, and we continued to seek other methods of alleviating severe tension without resorting to sedatives.

One method we still used with some patients was to administer small doses of insulin repeatedly over an eight-hour period, while giving them enough glucose and other foods to prevent them from undergoing more than a mild and prolonged insulin reaction. This required constant supervision by a skilled nurse and clearly had limited application outside our clinical setting. The old gun treatment (intravenous administration of both insulin and glucose) was sometimes effective. But some patients just had to sit it out and possibly rely on the protection of Antabuse to get them through these difficult periods.

About the same time that our business executive jolted us into our first clinical trial with adrenocortical extract, I began to receive regular long-distance calls from one of the first patients to receive Antabuse. As in the case of the businessman, this patient's addiction had progressed to the point that he experienced very severe withdrawal reactions whenever some physical or social crisis forced him to interrupt his compulsive drinking. He did not have the added complications of drug addiction, but he had managed to reach the "end of the road" without this complication. He explained that his wife had been a teetotaller when she married him. But she had tried to drink with him, became seriously addicted over the course of many years, and died during one of her bouts. Following that, he had practically ruined the family business, and he harbored an intense resentment toward his mother and sister, who had been trying for over a year to have him committed to an Ontario psychiatric hospital.

After his initial treatment and counseling with us, he remained undecided about whether to return home at all. He felt that he had lost everything and that there was no reason for him to go back. He finally decided to return long enough to sell the business and make plans to relocate elsewhere.

Our telephone conversations usually went something like this:

"Hello, Doc, is that you?. . . Doc, I can't take it anymore. I'm so tense I could blow apart. If it wasn't for that damned Antabuse, I'd be the drunkest man in the north country."

"How long is it since you last felt this way?" I would ask.

"About a month."

"How long did it last?"

"Three days."

"How long has this one been going?"

"Two days."

"Well, I guess you have another day to go. Stick with the Antabuse, call an AA friend, but for the love of God, don't spoil a winning combination!"

As he approached the end of his first dry year, he continued to call me, but later there was little of the desperation and urgency in his voice that had marked our earlier conversations. Eventually, he telephoned after an episode was over and he used a phrase I particularly liked. *"I've reached the other side* of another of those tense periods," he said.

We had a long talk about three years after his treatment began. In the interval he had completely restored the family business, paid off over $30,000 in debts, and had become reinstated in the community. I recall the highlights of that conversation:

"Are you still taking Antabuse?" I asked.

"No," he replied.

"How long did it take before you stopped using it?"

"Twenty-seven months."

"How long do you think you needed it?"

"About eighteen months."

"Why?"

"Well, I stopped having those tense periods altogether after eighteen months, but they really didn't cause me any trouble to speak of after the first year. I didn't know they were over for sure though, and I remembered your advice about holding onto a winning combination. That's why I kept on taking it for another nine months, just to be sure."

"Are you still active in AA?"

"Yes, very."

"Could an AA friend have helped you through those difficult times if you hadn't been taking Antabuse?"

"Not a chance! I was so desperate that the only reason I didn't drink was that it was physically impossible to. My AA friends were a help, but they alone couldn't have stopped me from drinking."

He told me about one of the most interesting developments of the entire three-year period. "You remember how angry I was at my mother and sister?" he said. "I hardly spoke to them at all during that first year, and just burned up whenever I thought of them trying to put me in a mental hospital. Around the eighteen-month period, about the same time that the dry drunks faded out, I realized that my resentment toward them was gone too. I could see that they had been desperate too and were trying to do the only thing they felt could be done. If they hadn't cared for me, they wouldn't have done anything. Now the whole situation has changed, and both Mom and my sister turn to *me* for help or advice whenever they need it!"

This patient remarried two years later, and until his death from heart disease twelve years after his treatment began, went on to have an active, constructive role in family and community affairs.

In October 1954, six months after we moved from Shadow Brook to the Bell Clinic, a paper was published in the *Canadian Medical Association Journal* by Dr. M. Wellman entitled "Management of the Late Withdrawal Symptoms of Alcohol." Wellman, a physician in the Canadian Navy, had observed some alcoholic patients for prolonged periods after their initial withdrawal from alcohol, and he noticed the resemblance between the recurrent episodes of tension and the original withdrawal reaction. I believe he was the first to use the phrase "late withdrawal symptoms" in referring to the conditions that my AA associates called "dry drunks."

In 1955 I gave an address to an open meeting in New Jersey on "An After-care and Rehabilitation Program for Alcohol Addicts." Afterwards, a tiny woman came up to ask some questions. She claimed that with the help of AA she had been dry for five years, and had continued to experience regular dry drunks for the entire period. I deduced that she had never received any medical advice, and that she was on a very poor diet, which left her as malnourished as she had been during her drinking period. I directed her to a physician for guidance in maintaining a careful nutritional regime that would include the proteins, vitamins, and minerals essential for any type of repair of tissue or function. Remembering my experiences up to that point, especially with our Willowdale Hospital patients, I suspected that there was some relationship between dry drunks and malnutrition.

When tranquilizer drugs came on the market, a wider selection of clinical tools became available to temporarily relieve severe states of tension. I came to expect episodes of more acute tension in those patients who had experienced the most extreme withdrawal reactions.

After speaking to an AA group one evening in the early 1950s, I was approached by a man who introduced himself as a physician and a member of AA. He said that he had read all he could find on the symptoms and treatment of alcohol addiction and had listened to medical papers on the subject, but he had yet to hear the problem of fatigue adequately discussed. He said that both before and after he had stopped drinking he had been tired to the point of utter exhaustion. He had also noticed serious fatigue in many of his AA associates, and he felt that this could be a serious problem for certain patients that could lead to discouragement, depression, and relapse.

The more carefully I looked for clinically significant fatigue during the first year of recovery, the more convinced I became that this physician was right. The idea was a logical one. Recovering alcoholics have usually experienced chronic intoxication, malnutrition, insomnia, and anxiety for long periods. After having abused their bodies so much, many patients experience fatigue and a severe reduction in their stress tolerance.

It appeared to me that the possibility of dangerous fatigue was most likely between the sixth and twelfth months of recovery, and I began to direct more attention to that period. We routinely recommended at least eight hours of daily rest and/or sleep during the first year. We cautioned hard-driving executives about using their lunch breaks for business rather than for proper nutrition and rest, and we suggested that they continue to practise the relaxation techniques they had learned. This advice was particularly appropriate for aggressive, impatient people who assumed that six months of abstinence could counteract ten or twenty years of damage. We also advised our patients to take in some protein every four hours during the working day. Not all of them paid attention the first time we told them.

An executive telephoned me from Montreal eight months after leaving our clinic. He was so exhausted that he could hardly make it home from work, and he was thoroughly discouraged by the effort of living without alcohol. When I questioned him about his habits, he admitted that he had continued to take work home with him, had made no attempt to rest at noon, and that he was not getting protein into his system every four hours. When he began to include some of these habits into his routine he was able to complete the transition from addiction to abstinence without further incident. Such cases made it more and more apparent to us why one of the AA slogans is "Easy Does It."

Recovering alcoholics often develop a low tolerance for further stress of any kind. In spite of this, many of them want to plunge into repairing their social and financial problems as soon as they are able to think clearly enough to recognize the extent of the devastation in their business and personal lives. I recall one man at the Alex G. Brown Clinic who outlined his plan to pay off his debts, set up a new household, and get his children back from the Children's Aid Society. In addition to maintaining contact with the clinic, going to AA meetings, and taking his Antabuse, he made arrangements to take on two full-time jobs — one during the day, and one in the evening. No amount of persuasion could convince him to modify his plan. He refused to believe that he did not have enough staying power for all the tasks he had set himself. Within three months he was back in prison, which I considered inevitable with the unrealistic regimen he had set for himself.

Of the three conditions — tension, fatigue, and loneliness — the one that has always intrigued me the most is loneliness. What is its clinical significance? How important is it in sustaining addiction and in impeding recovery? I became convinced that loneliness is a more consistent element of addiction to alcohol, drugs, and food than tension, fatigue, or anything else. My observations of the relationships in AA made me suspect that many people who had experienced loneliness were overcoming it through their new relationships in AA.

Sometimes patients attached themselves to the staff in our clinic. One unmarried woman in her late twenties arrived at our clinic for treatment. She was suffering severe withdrawal and had a grossly enlarged liver. She was also frightened and depressed, and very much alone. Her only living relative was her wealthy father, who had recovered from his own alcohol problem but who would have nothing to do with his only daughter, except to provide her with a generous living allowance. Her mother had died many years before, and as far as we could determine, she had no friends, work associates, or other relationships through church, clubs, politics, or community activity. In her isolation, she attached herself to the clinic staff like a frightened child. Her efforts to be helpful were sometimes more of a nuisance, however, and we soon realized that we had been adopted. Until she eventually stopped her visits some months later, her palpable loneliness posed some difficult problems for us, as well as for her.

Loneliness is every bit as serious an indication of disturbance in health and well-being as are pain and tension. Addiction, in all its manifestations, contributes to aloneness, a fact well illustrated by one of my patients I will mention shortly.

Conquering all three of these obstacles is still necessary to overcome addiction. And a person struggling with an addiction needs a higher goal as well as a guide to a positive way of living. After much reading I finally encountered the message I sought in a book entitled *Disputed Passage* by Lloyd C. Douglas. In this medical novel an older surgeon talks with a young intern and gives him some important advice: "A man's occupation should serve as an axis on which he revolves in a given social area in the capacity of a constructive humanitarian."

I would write this statement on the clinic blackboard and then point out to the patients that we could actually live in any place but somehow it had to be in relation to our job. Thus, our work largely determined those people that we would encounter over and over again. Our job became the axis upon which each one revolves in a given social area.

I suggested that the next consideration we all should have is this: how do people feel after they meet us? Do they feel better, or do they feel worse? Has meeting us been an uplifting experience for them, or has it somehow contributed to their anxiety, their frustration, their anger, their depression? Perhaps we are so caught up in our own problems and affairs that we don't have any real human contact with the majority of people we encounter — a "nothing" kind of experience. And finally, in the search for another approach to living, it is important for people to explore the possibility of feeling good by helping others as an alternative to feeling good from the effects of alcohol or drugs.

A prominent Toronto lawyer with a serious alcohol dependence came to our clinic as a patient. His wife had died a year or so earlier and he was still grieving for her. While he was at the clinic, it was very difficult to know whether he was benefitting from any of our talks or discussions, because he didn't participate at all. Nor did he come back for our weekly follow-up meetings.

I received a surprising telephone call from him, however, about six months after he had left. He started the conversation rather gruffly by saying, "I don't want you to think that you swept me off my feet with your eloquence, but I still remember clearly the talk you gave based on the quote from Lloyd C. Douglas' book. I was forced to face up to the fact that practically everyone I met felt worse after meeting me than before. Between grieving for my wife and my drinking, I had no time for my teenage son, who was doing poorly in high school. I was so surly when I walked into the office that the receptionist hated to see me come in, and that pretty well applied to my secretary and my law partners too.

"You forced me to ask myself the question, 'Do I have to be like this to practise law?' So I deliberately planned to change my approach to all of the people I encountered regularly. The first to benefit was my son, who has brightened up considerably and is now doing well at high school. The people at the office can't understand what has happened to me. There is a totally different expression on their faces now when they see me coming. I haven't been drinking, and I'm beginning to feel good in a new way, particularly since I've made more money in the last six months in my practice than in any six-month period in the past." I was delighted to hear of his success and asked him to please keep me informed.

A year after he left the clinic he telephoned again and said, "I want to set up an appointment to have a long talk with you." This was arranged. He announced that he was following the guidelines recommended in Lloyd C. Douglas' novel and that he was going to take the idea a step further by taking a holiday in Europe. He admitted that in the past he had tended to be abrupt and demanding of bellhops, waiters, and waitresses and that he was outspoken whenever he was annoyed by what he considered poor service. He said, "I am going to try to be different on this trip."

I went over his itinerary with him carefully pointing out that he had had one year of learning how to cope with situations at home in Toronto on an alcohol-free basis; had he given adequate thought to preparing for the plane trip and the alcoholic beverages he would encounter in Britain, France, and elsewhere in Europe? I strongly urged him not only to prepare for how he would turn down an offer of a drink but what he would ask for instead. And I asked him to please get in touch with me as soon as he returned, because I was most interested to hear how he had made out. He came back happy to report that his new approach had worked as effectively with strangers while he was on holiday as it had with his family and work associates.

In the early 1950s, during the period of my active involvement with the committee on alcoholism of the American Association of Industrial Physicians and Surgeons, a business executive from one of the major corporations in the United States became a patient. He was one of five division managers in a huge industrial complex. I was impressed by his high intelligence and obvious abilities. At that time I made it a policy to seek the opinion of many patients concerning the program and to ask for constructive comments on how it might be improved. Accordingly, I had a conversation with this gentleman shortly before he returned to the United States. One of his first comments was, "I am very glad that you have this drug, Antabuse, because until I find out what I am up against in learning how to live without alcohol, I don't want to take any unnecessary chances. Perhaps the most important thing that has happened to me has occurred without any conscious planning on your part at all."

He continued. "As you know, there are several younger patients here and they realize that I have an important job back home. Often after the rest of the clinic staff have gone home, they would ask for my advice on a wide range of problems and situations. I made certain that I didn't attempt to advise them about their drinking or what to do about it — that was your job — but I often felt that I could advise them on other business-related problems. Before long, I realized I was feeling good in a new way, and I thought, 'This is why I used to take alcohol — in order to feel good.'

"I was forced to come to a very painful conclusion: I had been so busy, so determined to get ahead in the business world, that I didn't go out of my way to help anybody. I was only interested in myself. I had got ahead quite rapidly. I came in contact with lots of people in as much trouble as the other patients in the clinic, but I had no time to worry about their problems.

"I realized that back home working for me and with me are all kinds of people with problems and feelings that can be hurt, either deliberately or by neglect. I am going to remember that they have feelings that can be hurt in my interaction with them, and to help them when I can. Before I worked for this corporation I was an editor and a writer, and I plan to use part of my former drinking time to write again. Now I know what I want to write about."

These were some of the cases reinforcing my belief that each person has the opportunity to become the axis for his or her own caring community. Those who succeed in transferring their dependence from one based on chemicals to one relying on people and who experience a new sense of well-being, are well on their way to total recovery.

We continued to emphasize pleasant, informal surroundings and a warm, understanding staff at Shadow Brook, and we maintained definite ground rules about patient-staff relationships from the beginning of each patient's admission. The first rule was that we should try to treat all patients in a friendly manner, but avoid showing favoritism, which was not always easy. We also had to keep in mind that, particularly in the early stages of treatment, these lonely patients were very capable of manipulating their environment to meet their immediate goals. Some even made an effort to achieve preferred status by offering gifts to one or more of the staff, or by inviting them to their homes. Others volunteered their help around the clinic.

The bottom line was that although we were brought into very close contact with the intimate personal needs of some very lonely people, we were careful to ensure that staff relationships remained uniformly supportive and therapeutic. We were personally important to our patients during a crucial transitional period in their lives, but we could not continue to function professionally if the relationships were allowed to become permanent.

I remember one patient from Ohio who was brought to Shadow Brook by his sister and her husband. He did not appear to be a very promising candidate for recovery, since according to his sister he had been living on skid row for several years. Their parents had been killed in an accident when they were very small, and the children had been placed in different foster homes. The sister had the good fortune to be taken into a home where she was wanted and loved, but her younger brother had encountered nothing but rejection and brutality in his foster home. He had run away at age fourteen. The brother confessed that by the time he was old enough to survive on his own he had acquired a deep distrust of everyone. Since he was incapable of enjoying the company of others, he began to mold his life around the pleasure that alcohol alone could provide. But even while drinking he remained a loner, and he usually rebuffed friendly overtures in taverns or bars. By the time he had reached his early twenties, his drinking was so out of control that it interfered with a succession of jobs, and by his late twenties he was on skid row. His hostile, defensive attitude toward other people was reinforced when he began to be pushed around by the police. From his standpoint, such treatment was to be expected.

Even though his sister had lost all trace of him when he was fourteen, she never gave up looking for him. She had married a kind, stable man who helped in her search, and together they looked until they finally found him in a distant part of the same state. Shortly thereafter, they brought him to our clinic.

About two weeks after the man had been admitted, we were having a chat when he said, "I can understand my sister, since she's a relative, but I can't figure that brother-in-law of mine. He's paying the bill for my treatment — but what's his angle? What's in it for him? He knows I have nothing. Sometimes I think maybe he doesn't have an angle. Maybe he's on the level and just wants to help. At other times I think he likely doesn't give a damn whether I live or die, and does this only to please his wife. You know, Doctor, I'm beginning to believe, though, that they're both on the level, and whenever I let myself believe this, I feel warm all over like I never felt before. Then I close up and say to myself, 'Don't be a fool; don't trust anybody,' and I go back to feeling cold again."

A week or so later we talked again. He said, "I can begin to see that I might be able to let other people into my life, but I'm always going to have problems. It's so natural for me to be suspicious of all people that I'll have to concentrate, or I'll insult anybody who tries to be a friend. It'll take a long time for me to get used to the idea that some people can be trusted and that I can enjoy the feeling of being liked and trusted too. So I see I have a double job to do. I have to learn how to live without alcohol, and how to like and trust people at the same time." When I heard from him a year or so later he was doing quite well with both projects.

The case of a very obese patient who had become addicted to Dexedrine served to remind us that people can choose comfort in drugs or alcohol to overcome loneliness. The drug had originally been prescribed to control her appetite, and by the time she came to us she was locked into an uncontrollable desire for both food and Dexedrine. She hesitated to deal with either one. When a nurse finally persuaded her to shake the last crumbs of Dexedrine from her purse, she said sadly, "I hate to do this. I love them: they do things for me that people have never been able to do!"

On the basis of these and countless other incidents, we shaped our basic treatment philosophy around the idea of trying to replace chemicals with people. "In times of trouble, turn to a person instead of a chemical" became our standard advice. The patients who seemed to learn from this philosophy and to adopt it usually overcame their addictions.

One patient in particular stands out in my mind. I was called to Shadow Brook at 5:00 A.M. on a wet, windy fall morning to admit a patient from a distant part of the province (who turned out to be a physician). He was comatose, bluish-gray in color, cold, clammy, and breathing with great difficulty. No air seemed to be reaching the lower half of his lungs, and his heart and blood pressure showed alarming abnormalities. I called Dr. Bill Hall, who came over to see him at once. We decided that it would take less time and be less stressful for the patient if we had an oxygen tent sent to us rather than try to transfer him to a general hospital. But there was only slight improvement when he was put into the tent. In spite of our efforts, he did not respond to any treatment, remained in a coma, and died the following day. The postmortem examination revealed collapse of the lower lobes of both lungs, with evidence of infection in other parts of the lungs.

I finally got the whole story of the man's illness after his death. He had been addicted to morphine for many years until the authorities caught up with him and cancelled his privilege to prescribe narcotics. Since he had no contact with the illicit narcotics trade, this action effectively cut off his source of supply. Very few people in the area realized that their family doctor was addicted to morphine, since drunkenness and poor judgment are not marked by-products of this type of addiction. When he was cut off from his source he became desperate and turned to alcohol and barbiturates. The most noticeable result of this shift in dependence was that he was obviously drunk much of the time and quite unable to carry on his practice.

The night before his admission, he had taken an overdose of alcohol and the sedative Seconal, the effects of which had almost produced respiratory arrest. He vomited and breathed in some of the vomitus, which blocked the air passages to the lower lobes. By the time he reached us there was very little that could be done to save him. I often wondered what the legal system had gained by cutting off his morphine without providing him with any treatment for his addiction or its related problems.

Patients like this physician reminded us of just how little we knew about addiction rather than how much, and how important it was to provide more than just band-aid solutions to addiction problems. Although we had already achieved widespread recognition for our efforts, we still had far to go and I sensed that the Shadow Brook period had to end. The operating costs were too high, the private sanitarium license imposed unnecessary administrative problems, and I wanted one clinic for both sexes.

One of the Shadow Brook patients, who had recovered from his addiction to both alcohol and sedative drugs, was keenly interested in our search for better treatment methods, and he gave me some excellent advice: "Always remember that a true friend is one who will point out your mistakes; any damned fool can pat you on the back!" Since there were so few clinics in those days trying to deal with addiction problems, it was easy for us to "stand out" and to regard any success as the logical result of our efforts. It was difficult to find someone to tell us what we might be doing wrong and how we could improve our success rate.

It was an AA friend from Detroit who had been dry for over ten years who pointed out that a certain percentage of alcohol addicts had always been able to stop drinking on their own — long before AA or modern clinics had come into being. He suggested that our best successes might have been achieved with the patients who least required our services. The polite implication, of course, was that perhaps we were not doing so well with those who most needed help. Rather than failing too often in those days for our efforts to be considered worthwhile, though, I knew that we were making some progress in the addiction field and I could point to a few positive results. Many of those who had passed through Glenmaple, Shadow Brook, and the Willowdale Hospital were now leading happy, productive lives. Occasional comments of this kind, however, and my interest in the research being carried out by Ward Smith led me in a new direction.

It was obvious that the higher the level of alcohol in a person's system, the greater the health dysfunction. While I began exploring how to prevent people from ingesting such large amounts of alcoholic beverages, Ward Smith and his associates were trying to measure the point at which an individual becomes intoxicated by analyzing blood-alcohol levels. We decided to explore together the development of a formula that could estimate drinkers' intake patterns, and a device that could warn them when they might be heading toward serious health problems, recurrent impairment in judgment or motor skills, or both. We wanted to develop a preventive technique so that people could judge their drinking patterns and the hazards associated with their alcohol intakes.

I was not so naive as to believe that a person who was already an alcoholic could be helped by this new research and the formula we hoped to develop. Behind all of my thinking was my primary concern with total health and the prevention of alcohol-related problems, and my belief that the outcome of our research would contribute to comprehensive health-care programs.

My interest in finding a tangible means of measuring alcohol levels was stimulated when I was asked to prepare an article for the student medical journal at the University of Toronto. The suggested topic was a discussion of the effects of varying alcohol levels on different people. For the next few months Ward Smith and I tested all the Shadow Brook patients at the time of their admission and recorded some astonishing results. One patient was still on his feet, although extremely unsteady, with an alcohol level in excess of 0.4 percent in his bloodstream. (At that time 0.15 percent was considered the upper limit of safety for operating a motor vehicle; the legal limit in Canada is now about half that, or 0.08 percent.)

I had become intrigued with the possibility of estimating alcohol levels without having to do a blood test. If, as claimed then, the level of alcohol in the bloodstream was largely determined by three factors — body weight, the amount of alcohol consumed, and the length of time spent consuming it — I thought it would be possible to devise a formula to estimate that level without having to draw blood. This seemed particularly logical, since the theory was that alcohol loss from oxidation and excretion occurred at about the same rate for any individual regardless of those three variables.

I can lay very little claim to being a mathematician; however, I finally produced a formula by trial and error. As usual, I was working against a tight deadline to develop the formula and submit my article on time. I felt fairly safe in our findings, although I was not sure the formula could withstand much scientific scrutiny. I reasoned that since the journal had limited circulation to a select, well-educated group, any serious miscalculation would soon be discovered and pointed out to me so that it could be corrected. I therefore awaited the reaction to the article with some misgivings. As expected, I received a call the morning after it appeared in the journal, but not from anyone at the University of Toronto. To my horror, it came from the medical section of *Time* magazine in New York. The magazine wanted to prepare a story on my formula for the March issue, which was then in preparation. I telephoned Ward Smith in a near panic. He promptly referred me to the best mathematician he knew, his boss, Ken Ferguson. Ken suggested I come down to his office right away.

I arrived at Ken's office in the early afternoon. He immediately dropped everything he was doing, and we worked on the formula without stopping until close to midnight. At first he was doubtful about its feasibility, but after testing the formula exhaustively against published blood/alcohol curves showing the actual rate at which alcohol left the bodies of the subjects tested, we began to breathe more easily. We made some minor changes to it, which made me far more confident when I met the *Time* reporter. The report appeared in March 1953. The formula was:

$$L = \frac{7000A}{W} - 13T,$$ where

L = the number of milligrams of alcohol in every 100 c.c.s of blood;
A = the intake of pure alcohol in ounces;
W = the body weight in pounds; and
T = the number of hours from the onset of drinking.

Since we had survived that ordeal, I suggested to Ken that if we could design a formula, we should also be able to make a slide rule. (This was long before the days of sophisticated computers.) He agreed to be responsible for the mathematics and design, while I was to work on the instructions for its use. In fact, we formed a partnership just in case the idea might eventually produce some financial rewards — a hope that was never fulfilled. We eventually produced a working model and agreed, after much discussion, to call it an "alco-dial." In the meantime the medical reporter for *Time* was interested further in the formula story, and he contacted us again early in 1954. When he learned that Ken and I had produced the alco-dial, and that Ken had prepared a paper on it that was to appear in the March issue of *Chemistry in Canada*, he convinced *Time* to publish another story about our research to coincide with the publication of Ken's article. *Time* had titled its March 1953 article, "How High Am I?" It began as follows:

> "Don't drink too much" is a common bit of medical advice, but the trick has been for a man to learn how much is too much. Now a Canadian physician, Robert Gordon Bell, who has treated thousands of alcoholics, offers a formula which he believes any intelligent person can use as a rough guide to keep his drinking within safe and sane limits. Most people, he holds, will be less likely to drink too much if they are made to think about the problem and can learn where the danger point is.

The article explained our formula and concluded:

> Dr. Bell emphasizes that individuals differ enormously in their ability to "hold" liquor, e.g. a scrawny, 120-pounder may be able to outdrink a heavyweight wrestler. But if the body is repeatedly subjected to massive doses of alcohol, sooner or later it can no longer adapt itself to the stress, and metabolism breaks down. Warns Dr. Bell: "Anybody who repeatedly drinks so that he has a higher concentration than 50 milligrams should take a look at his drinking habits." Always moderate in his own drinking, Dr. Bell has cut down still since he started to see milligrams in every glass. There is another handy feature to his formula: Anybody who is too far gone to work it out is too far gone.

The report in the March 1954 issue of *Time* was brief:

> Ontario's Dr. Robert G. Bell has devised a handy "alco-dial" to help tipplers decide whether they are in condition to drive home. The subject turns the arrow to the number of drinks (jiggers of hard liquor or cans of beer) he has had, then reads off

> the amount of alcohol in his blood on a circular dial, next to his body weight. Readings up to 50 milligrams of alcohol per 100 grams of blood are safe, from 50 to 100 doubtful (caution is indicated). When the gauge points to more than 100, the subject should promptly get off the road. If he can't remember, he should ask to be taken home.

The March 1954 article gave us wide publicity indeed, particularly after a story on both the formula and alco-dial by the Associated Press was picked up across North America. However, I was disappointed that *Time* had not given credit to Ken Ferguson, whose name also appears on the invention.

By this time I had become so immersed in considering the factors affecting levels of alcohol in the body that I had difficulty appreciating how little the average person knew about the subject. My first instructions turned out to be totally inadequate for most people, but fortunately we had not invested too much in the first model of the alco-dial. We were literally flooded with requests for distribution rights from many different parts of the world after the media publicity. Although we held world copyright on the alco-dial and probably could have made a handsome profit on it, we concluded that we should turn down all requests. The alco-dial had been prepared in the hope that it could become a reliable tool for use in a variety of health and safety programs, but it was not yet ready for widespread general use. It was too difficult for a layperson to use properly, which meant that it would have been an overnight sensation and nothing more. Mary agreed with the decision, although she was disappointed because of our precarious financial situation.

I continued to revise the instructions for the alco-dial from time to time in the following years. I finally produced a model with detailed instructions that just about anyone could understand. But by this time the original interest had long passed, although various police forces had been using it routinely.

In the meantime, Ward Smith had been the director of the attorney-general's crime laboratory for Ontario since August 1951. Eventually he became internationally recognized for his work in the forensic sciences but he still retained a position on the teaching staff of the pharmacology department. His interest in the estimation of alcohol levels in the bloodstream remained, and he was now able to relate it to traffic accidents and crime. Ward usually asked me to be his medical assistant whenever he undertook major research. This gave me the opportunity to share in the benefits of his studies and in a number of his experiments.

On one such occasion, Ward invited a few friends to a party, with the promise of plenty of booze, on the understanding that they would drink as much as possible for two hours, after which they were to breathe into Borkenstein's Breathalyzer, a U.S. invention. The guests also had to allow me to take a blood sample at the same time, and to agree to let somebody sober drive them home. Jack Macdonald and my brother-in-law, Vincent Lamping, were our guinea pigs on only one occasion. Due to the hangovers from their first experience we could not persuade them to repeat the test, no matter how hard we tried to appeal to their interest in forwarding the cause of science.

Over the course of those years, Ward was having a great deal of trouble persuading judges and magistrates that the breathalyzer results should be permitted as legal evidence in connection with traffic violations. He had already trained the Ontario Provincial Police in the use of both the breathalyzer and the alco-dial, and they became particularly adept at alco-dial calculations. When a driver was stopped, the police would check his alcohol level using the breathalyzer, then roughly guess his body weight. They could then use the alco-dial to make a fairly accurate assessment of the number of drinks in the driver's system

My father and mother, Robert and Elizabeth Bell, circa 1911.

Me, at about eighteen months.

Bellwood, the Bell family homestead where I grew up, near St. Marys, Ontario.

In 1923, at age twelve, I began high school at St. Marys Collegiate.

A light moment during the summer of 1931, when I worked as a set-up man for the traveling Chautauqua program.

The two GBs in the early 1930s. My high-school friend, George Birtch, later aided in the programs of both Donwood and Bellwood.

Mary's and my wedding day in Port Colborne, June 18, 1938.

With my sister Jean and brother Oliver (right) on Jean's graduation from nurses' training, June 5, 1940.

At the urging of my men in the #1 Psychological Unit of the Brampton Conditioning Centre, I was outfitted in a smart new uniform (April 1944).

With Aunt Jessie, Mary, Ronnie, and baby Jan, circa 1946.

Our first clinic, Glenmaple, open from September 1946 to December 1947.

Shadow Brook, our second clinic, open from December 1947 to May 1954.

Booth sponsored by the Committee on Problem Drinking, circa 1954. I was chairman of this committee for seven years, part of my involvement with the American Association of Industrial Physicians and Surgeons.

The Alex G. Brown Clinic in Mimico, outside Toronto, where I worked as consultant for their treatment and rehabilitation program from spring 1951 to the early 1960s.

Receiving the Malvern Institute of Pennsylvania's citation of merit, our first award for our work with addicted patients, in November 1958.

The Bell Clinic, originally the Willowdale Hospital for female patients, was licensed to admit male patients as well in April 1954.

The Donwood Institute opened in March 1966.

We celebrated the birth of the new Donwood Foundation at a special luncheon in 1967. At my table were (left to right) Bill Ford, Mary Epp, Ken Ferguson, John B. Parkin, and Harvey Firestone, Jr.

Receiving the Order of Canada from Governor General Edward Shreyer in Ottawa, December 1982.

With my daughter, Linda, now business manager of Bellwood Health Services Inc.

The Bell family, 1984.

at that time. When a person with a level of 0.15 percent alcohol asserted that he had consumed "just a couple of beers," the police could quickly check his honesty.

Ward finally persuaded the local judiciary to co-operate with his department in a test. The judges and magistrates were invited to a cocktail party, and on the way out each of them was asked to blow into the breathalyzer, which was operated by a police officer. The policeman made a quick guess of each man's weight, and by using the alco-dial could tell him how many drinks he had just consumed. The experiment was a complete success. To the astonishment of the "guests," most of the estimates were right on the nose, which led Ward to remark, "We've struck another blow for freedom!" I don't recall that the experiment had any immediate or significant effect, although eventually the legal limit for impaired driving was set at a level of 0.08 percent alcohol in the bloodstream.

It was about the time of the alco-dial studies that I began to feel the need to assume complete responsibility for all aspects of operating a clinic to treat addictions. Although Bruce Davidson and I had an excellent relationship, he did own the entire Shadow Brook operation, and I was his employee. I wanted to be free to make all the decisions, and to proceed in any directions I deemed appropriate. For this and other reasons, I finally decided to explore the possibility of shutting down Shadow Brook entirely.

One of the other factors was that the non-medical costs at Shadow Brook were too high. The heating bill alone at the estate ran into thousands of dollars each winter, a staggering sum in those days. In fact, on more than one occasion, Bruce Davidson had to make up for an operating deficit out of his own pocket, and never during the six years of its operation did Shadow Brook do more than break even.

Moreover, as had been the case at Glenmaple, we were having regular trouble with the septic tanks at both

Shadow Brook and Willowdale Hospital. Whenever this happened, there was a marked drop in morale and enthusiasm among both patients and staff. The local sewer repairman knew us so well that we were on a first-name basis.

There was another problem that was causing increasing concern. The Three Point Club had been granted sole responsibility for the continuing-therapy program too soon — before the members had recovered sufficiently from their uncontrolled compulsion to drink. In spite of the club's name and its implications, the members' efforts became directed increasingly at the re-establishment of their old social life (minus alcohol) which for them was a non-rewarding endeavor, with the old cementing ingredient of that lifestyle missing. This gradually led its leaders to compromise their attitudes about the importance of total abstinence.

But I reached my final decision to resign from Shadow Brook only after lengthy discussions with my closest friends and advisors. One of them was Jack Miller, a very capable corporation lawyer who had protected us from legal misadventures just as Ken Ferguson, Bill Hall, Jean Davey, and others aided us in our clinical and theoretical problems. Jack had helped us in the purchase of Willowdale Hospital, and was beginning to take our unusual predicaments as a matter of course.

I finally summoned up the courage to tell Bruce Davidson I was going to resign. Disappointed, he could not understand why I wouldn't try to work out the problems instead of running away from them. The members of the Three Point Club were even more upset, and sent a delegation to Bruce to explore the possibility of finding another medical director. Mary was also worried, because we were giving up the only financial security we had ever known, slight though it was. Our staff members were also concerned about their futures. Once again, it seemed, the Bells would be right back where we had been before — in a highly uncertain new situation.

CHAPTER TEN

The Bell Clinic

*A*fter deciding to resign from Shadow Brook, I gave serious consideration to seeking full-time work in industrial medicine. I had few illusions left about the hazards of working in the addiction field, and I was increasingly aware that my family was receiving much less than their proper share of my time. By now we had four children, Ronald, Janice, Linda, and Mary. If I ever wanted to break away from the addiction-treatment field, this seemed to be my last chance, because once we proceeded to open a new clinic, we would be committed to dealing with the problems of addiction more deeply than ever. But even as I considered our next step, deep down I knew there was no turning back.

I formulated a plan and took it to the Ontario Ministry of Health. It called for combining the Shadow Brook and Willowdale Hospital operations into an in-patient and out-patient service for both men and women, using the Willowdale Hospital license and location. The site had the advantage of being close to public transportation, which made it much more suitable than Shadow Brook for the development of an out-patient program. We could also increase our in-patient quota from seven to nine by closing in the verandah and making other alterations to the building. By this time both we and the ministry were convinced that men and women could be treated successfully under the same roof, so we were granted permission. After consulting Dr. Arthur Kelly, Ken Ferguson, and a few others, we decided that the new venture should be called the Bell Clinic. Our old friend Mac helped us secure the extra credit to make the alterations to the building, and the move was made on April 1, 1954 — April Fool's Day! I was delighted to learn later that Bruce Davidson was able to sell the Shadow Brook property at a profit, but sad that there would not be enough room at the Bell Clinic for the entire Shadow Brook staff. My brother-in-law, Vincent, and his wife, Helen, who had managed the hectic business office throughout the entire Shadow Brook period, went off in a new direction, as did many of the others.

During those first two years at the Bell Clinic, we were not sure we had made the right decision. Although my family and friends understood my reasons for leaving Shadow Brook, a transition from a twenty-five-bed institution in a beautiful setting to nine beds in a modest home was not generally regarded as a progressive step. The Three Point Club was now without a home, and its members supported the new venture with limited enthusiasm. The patient load fluctuated, and it was extremely difficult to find enough revenue to meet current expenses and pay off old debts. We hadn't been operating there for very long before Mac advised us to get a new auditor and start keeping monthly statements. We took his advice. From then on we did not have to wonder from month to month if we were in financial difficulties; we knew it for sure.

Another old problem reared its ugly head. In spite of a new tile bed, the septic tank proved unequal to the extra load, and we were again plunged into a pungent awareness of the hazards of a suburban enterprise. As I supervised the installation of yet another larger and more costly tile bed, I swore that never again would I try to operate a hospital that could not be connected to sewers. A few months later, in the summer of 1955, the township put in a sanitary-sewer line within ten feet of our property. In spite of the fact we were still paying off our king-sized private system, we welcomed the opportunity to go further into debt in order to escape septic tanks forever.

Mary continued to struggle with accounts, cooks, housekeepers, and handymen as she had before. The first few cooks at the Bell Clinic were either very crotchety, unreliable, or both. Typical of the lot was an Austrian chap who answered one of her ads. He was a suave, easygoing person who gave the impression of having moved in elite circles in an assortment of world capitals. Unfortunately, his competence as a cook left something to be desired: he seemed more skilled at preparing hors d'oeuvres than a balanced diet for malnourished addicts. He was unhappy whenever he was too far from the bright lights of the city, and he obviously regarded Willowdale as a remote outpost. He had been with us about a week when he strolled over to our house one evening after work and was astonished to find Mary, the four children, Mary Epp, and me all out on the roof. I cheerfully explained to him that we had come up to see a family of raccoons that was living in an unused chimney. That was apparently the final straw. Muttering to himself, he strolled out the lane and kept going. We never saw him again.

Although the monthly statements gradually began to improve a little, our old bank manager was worried. He had stuck with us through our Willowdale Hospital period and had absorbed the extra cost of remodeling the Bell Clinic, but he was worried about our ability to retire our bank loan as rapidly as we had hoped. On top of this, we had been forced to purchase another house for extra office space and sleeping accommodation for out-of-town patients. After reassuring the neighbors once more about our operation and having a by-law amended to permit us to use the building for this purpose, we had Jack Miller, our lawyer, arrange for an issue of preferred stock to finance the purchase, remodeling, and furnishing of the house. Most of the shares were bought by former patients.

In spite of the fact that my wife, Mary, donated her services as manager of the Bell Clinic, we were in continuous financial difficulties for the first thirty months. Finally, our banker concluded that he could no longer back us. Mary, Mac, and I held what turned out to be an historic board meeting. Mac suggested that we were dealing with the wrong branch of the wrong bank. He said, "In that particular branch, yours is a fairly big account, and any problems you have stand out like a sore thumb to the management. Let's try to find a bank in downtown Toronto accustomed to accounts so large that *your* financial woes will seem small."

One of our former patients was a branch manager for the Royal Bank of Canada in Toronto. He agreed to take over our account and to grant us a loan sufficient to pay off all our creditors. So began our relationship with the Royal Bank, which has provided us with financial support in times of crisis ever since. With the help of our new banker, we gradually paid off the loan, whittled away at the mortgages, and eventually bought back the preferred stock. But it took quite a while.

There have been many times throughout the years, both in Canada and the United States, when young physicians have told me that they would like to set up a private clinic or hospital, to be on their own like I was. My reply has usually been, "More power to you, but listen to your banker and business associates before you start. Your medical degree has not equipped you to cope with even fifty percent of the financial and administrative problems you will encounter."

When we started up the Bell Clinic we had more than just financial and administrative worries to contend with. Although some doctors then were sympathetic to the plight of alcoholics, most physicians in Canada and the United States were still not prepared to become involved in such a controversial area of health care. In general, medical professionals in the mid-1950s distanced themselves from the problems associated with alcoholism, and I remained a maverick of sorts to my peers.

Whenever possible I tried to attend medical association meetings to keep abreast of developments in the health-care field. Frequently when I approached the bar at these functions for my usual glass of Scotch someone would blurt out, "Don't tell me you take a drink!" or "I thought you belonged to the temperance group!" I was annoyed that I had never come up with an appropriate reply on these occasions and I used to fume about it afterward. I made up my mind that I would be ready the next time a physician made such a remark. The opportunity finally arose at a medical meeting held in the Park Plaza Hotel in Toronto. When I went up to the bar for a drink before dinner, someone said, "Don't tell me you're taking a drink!" I replied, "I suppose you'd be surprised if a urologist had to urinate!" The retort effectively squashed any further conversation, and word must have spread, because I was rarely accosted with such remarks again.

If I wasn't generally accepted by the medical profession, at least I received encouragement from other unexpected quarters. In the late fifties the Canadian Headmasters Association held their annual meeting at Upper Canada College in Toronto. Their host, the headmaster of UCC had invited me to give an address. I clearly remember his remarks when I finished my talk: "It has been a unique experience for a group of headmasters to receive a lesson in teaching from a physician."

I was really thrilled — a compliment for a change. For over ten years I had been giving lectures almost daily and leading discussions with my alcoholic patients and had been guided only by their frank responses to my efforts. This had become a routine exercise in mutual understanding and I had no idea that the methods I had developed would impress such an august body as the association representing the headmasters of the private schools in Canada.

We were still not widely accepted in medical circles. During the Shadow Brook and early Bell Clinic periods, there was basically one reasonably reliable source of competent, part-time medical staff. These were physicians who had completed their junior internships and were preparing for a specialty. Although many were married, they received very little pay for their long hours of service in the teaching hospitals, and they welcomed the chance to be on call at all hours for us on a fee-for-service basis. In return for gaining experience and training in caring for addicted patients, they also kept us aware of the new therapeutic developments in other areas. Over the years, as pay and working conditions for interns improved, it became increasingly difficult to attract their services. Even so, Dr. Bill Hall and Dr. Jean Davey still managed to steer a succession of bright young physicians our way and they kept the medical part of our program functioning at a high level of competence. They also continued to make it possible for us to transfer seriously ill patients to St. Michael's Hospital or Women's College Hospital, where our consultants could treat them.

The nurses at the Bell Clinic still took the history of all the patients being admitted, as they had done at Shadow Brook, and they continued to care for them through the difficult first few days. We had come to expect a general pattern of defensiveness in most patients during the early stages of their treatment, and we appreciated more than ever the importance of the nurses in their role of introducing suspicious patients to a radically different medical environment. In addition, our nurses assumed the roles of laboratory technicians, interns, social workers, administrators, and family counselors. Fortunately, we had no trouble in the 1950s finding nurses to handle special assignments involving the management of delirium tremens or other serious complications.

The second phase of our treatment plan continued in much the same way it had at Shadow Brook. I gave a lecture five mornings a week (when I was not traveling); Mary Epp conducted a group-relaxation period every day after lunch; a film on some aspect of health or addiction was shown about three times weekly; and informal discussions introduced patients to the goal of improved health in all areas.

Individual counseling was an exercise in ingenuity requiring the genius of a Solomon. It often revealed that addiction might be a secondary, rather than a primary, problem, and these sessions could include advice on everything from mortgages to marriage. One young couple had traveled about fifty miles in search of advice. Their marriage was so close to breaking up that both had sought legal advice about separation or divorce. They were both about thirty years of age and had small children. He was the tall, lanky, outdoors type with an angry, stubborn expression and a reluctance to discuss personal problems with a stranger. She was a stunningly beautiful woman, and one of the liveliest — and angriest — I had ever met. My first few minutes with them convinced me that the interview would have to be conducted with each one separately.

I began with the woman. She was upset mainly about her husband's recurrent drunkenness and an affair he had been having with another woman. On the surface, the affair appeared to be problem enough, and she certainly made the most of painting herself as the injured party. She described her rival as an older, heavier, unattractive woman with a placid, cow-like disposition. She said that her husband's drinking had become more serious after she had found out about the affair, and she had exploded. When she finally paused, looking a little relieved, I ended the interview with her and ushered in her husband.

After some time, the man finally told me that his wife was capable of normal sexual relations, but that she had entered marriage with some very puritanical attitudes. He had begun to suspect that she was following her mother's advice to ration her sexual services to him as a reward for doing what she asked, but she justified her restraint by reminding him that sex was essentially a sinful activity. In complete frustration, he had sought solace from a totally different type of woman, one who made no demands of any kind on him. He admitted he drank heavily, but readily agreed to stop drinking altogether for a few months. He also agreed to discontinue seeing the other woman for the time being and to co-operate with any gestures his wife might make to repair their relationship.

Then I recalled the woman for a second interview. I began by asking her if she had ever taken off her clothes and examined herself carefully in a full-length mirror. She was speechless. Blushing deeply, she finally sputtered, "Why, Doctor, what do you mean?"

"I mean have you ever made an honest, objective appraisal of your truly remarkable charms?"

While she was still searching for an answer, I hit her with another: "Do you realize that, in addition to all your physical assets, you are an unusually passionate woman?"

"How do you know that?" she blurted out.

I told her that she had clearly demonstrated a capacity for intense emotion during our first hour-long interview, and that she was too healthy a person to be capable of it in one area and not in others. "How often have you taken the initiative in the sexual act, and how do you use all those physical and emotional assets?"

When she said that she had never taken the initiative, I told her it was time we had a serious talk about some of the basic principles of marital adjustment.

Now that her embarrassment was over, I could be even more explicit: "You have both admitted to me that you care deeply for each other in spite of your present problems. So I want you to keep him so "busy" that he'll trip over a match-stick, so busy he won't have the strength to walk to her place, let alone be any good when he gets there. Come back and see me in a week."

They returned a week later. She came tripping in, full of life and sparkle; he lumbered along behind her with a foolish grin on his face. I saw her just long enough to learn that she had done what I suggested. Then I interviewed her husband. I doubt if I have ever seen a more remarkable change in a man in just one week.

"Gee, Doc," he said to me, "I don't know what you told her, but things sure are different around home!" When I asked him about the other woman, he seemed a little startled at first, as if he didn't know to whom I was referring. She was certainly out of the picture now.

In a later interview with the husband, I suggested that he continue to abstain from drinking for at least several months, after which time he could try drinking in moderation. But first he had to explain the situation to his wife. We agreed that if his drinking got out of control without any marital difficulties, it would prove that the alcohol part of the problem was more advanced than we had thought, and that he would require further help. I saw them at monthly intervals for a while, and they seemed to be gradually developing a less intense, more normal relationship. My last contact with them was a few years later; they were getting along well and he was taking an occasional drink without any apparent negative effects.

We had other patients at the Bell Clinic who had combined alcohol and sex problems. Of course, we couldn't be as successful with all our patients as we were with this couple. One of our patients was a tall man in his late fifties. He had spent many years in India with the British Army, an experience that had wrought truly remarkable changes in his liver. He presented himself to us for treatment only with great reluctance and embarrassment, having to admit he could no longer hold his liquor like a gentleman.

We discovered that he had been trying to control the shakes with barbiturates, and that he had developed a full-blown case of barbiturate addiction to add to his already complicated clinical problems. Whereas the thought of no alcohol was alarming to him, the notion of no barbiturates threw him into a panic. We had to ease him down so gradually that he was on placebos for over a week before I dared tell him that drugs had been completely withheld from him. Even then he reacted with great alarm. This man was one of those individuals who greatly increased our respect for the overwhelming power of barbiturate dependency.

In later years we observed similar states of apprehension in patients addicted to tranquilizers.

I continued to see this patient for many months. Although he was quite friendly, it was difficult for him to discuss personal matters. But on one occasion about six months after we had begun treating him, he seemed to be particularly restless and perturbed. He harrumphed and snorted around my office for a few minutes, then blurted out rather obliquely: "I find it damnably boring to be reduced to song!" He was not happy when I explained to him that the same process that had given his liver such a beating could have irreversible effects on other parts of the body, and that it was unlikely we could help with that problem as well.

The Bell Clinic brought with it other novel and challenging addiction problems. During the Glenmaple, Shadow Brook, and Willowdale Hospital days from 1946 to 1954 we had had a few patients who were addicted to both alcohol and barbiturates. Their withdrawal reactions were similar to those of alcohol addiction alone, but offered a greater threat of convulsions. We also encountered our first amphetamine addict at the Bell Clinic — the first patient we had seen who was addicted to a stimulant instead of to a depressant. We were completely unsuccessful in helping him cope with his addiction and the related problems.

The 1950s produced a new class of depressant drugs called tranquilizers. Soon we began to admit patients addicted to alcohol together with one or more tranquilizers. The benzodiazipams — Valium, Librium, etc. — arrived on the scene in the early 1960s and became so popular that they quickly replaced the older depressants. By the time the Donwood Institute opened its doors in 1967, addiction to alcohol plus Valium-type drugs was becoming common. Since the mid-1960s there has been such a proliferation of new "uppers," "downers," and painkillers that we now encounter an amazing variety of combinations of old and new drugs to which our patients have become addicted.

The continuing-therapy program at the Bell Clinic was brought under the control of our clinical staff. As part of that program we urged all our patients to keep a diary as an aid in policing their old thoughts, particularly during the hazardous first year. We knew that only a fraction of them could be expected to keep a daily record of their thoughts and emotions consistently enough to do any good, so we devised a system of shorthand. Patients were shown how to record thoughts of drinking, degrees of tension, hours of sleep, medication, and other significant data simply by marking numbers around the day's date on a bedside calendar. With this basic code, they could keep their daily chart in only a few seconds before retiring. They were asked to mail their calendar records each month to Mary Epp, who was in charge of the program. She wrote personal notes in return, with newsletters we sent out, commented on the calendar entries, and acted as a friend and counselor to hundreds of patients and their families over the years. On many occasions patients have told me that they had been on the verge of giving up hope when Mary's reassuring note arrived in the mail. I continued to give refresher talks on Wednesday evenings and prepared the newsletter, which was sent out weekly to patients who lived too far away to attend our out-patient sessions. Besides these activities, much of my time in those days was spent seeing new patients, trying to cope with administrative problems as they arose, attempting to collect my thoughts so that I could come up with a decent blueprint for the treatment of addiction, and making numerous trips to a variety of institutions in the United States.

Ever since *Time*'s article about the alco-dial I had found my work increasingly recognized as I traveled in the United States. In 1955 the new California State Commission on Alcoholism invited me to address their members. At that time it was claimed that the incidence of alcoholism in California was double that for the country as a whole. In that same year the United States ranked second internationally in alcoholism, exceeded only by France.

When I arrived in California I learned that one of the reasons for the invitation was that the commissioners wanted to look me over as a possible director of their new organization. I was surprised by the suggestion that I present their case to the entire state assembly in Sacramento. Their argument was that I had much more experience in the field than any of them and was more experienced in speaking to large audiences as well. I did address the state assembly, but never seriously considered moving to California.

While I was there, I was also invited to address the San Francisco Press Club, a renowned institution with some very interesting traditions. One concerned "the black cat." When I arrived at the club for my engagement, I was asked if I would like to speak "behind the black cat."

"What does that mean?" I asked.

My hosts pointed to a statue of a black cat about two feet long and a foot or more high, lying in a relaxed position. The club honored a tradition whereby anyone who asked to speak behind the black cat could say anything he or she wished and it would not be reported in any media. I was told that President Roosevelt's son had once addressed the club and revealed that his father was planning to run for a third term as president of the United States. Because he had asked to speak behind the black cat, the news was not reported. I told my hosts that I would be delighted to address members of the press on those terms. As a token of the occasion, I was presented with a small replica of the cat about three inches long. That little black cat has sat on my office desk for thirty-four years now. From time to time I talk with prominent people in the business or political world who seem to be reluctant to tell me certain things that are bothering them. Whenever I think it appropriate, I ask if they would prefer to converse with me "behind the black cat."

Now that I was doing so much traveling I had to rely more than ever on the two Marys to keep the Bell Clinic functioning smoothly. My wife remained very active at the clinic while continuing to run our household and care for the children. She kept a close watch on our financial situation and assumed responsibility for the administration of the clinic.

Mary Epp made sure that the clinical end of the operation functioned smoothly. It would have been impossible for me to undertake all of my out-of-clinic activities without knowing that she could handle any crisis in my absence. Not only was she decisive and unflappable; she could handle most of our patients far better than anyone else on our staff — including me. On one occasion at the Bell Clinic we ran short of suitable medical help. One physician did volunteer to pitch in at a time when I had to attend a meeting in California. He was a recovering patient himself from northern Ontario who had arranged to stay in Toronto after we released him. He agreed to look after physical examinations and medical emergencies while I was away, while he was continuing therapy for his own dependence. Mary Epp called me in California to tell me that the recovering doctor had reported for work dead drunk.

"Put him to bed, sober him up, and hold the fort until I return," I said, without the slightest hesitation. She did not let me down. When I returned to Toronto a few days later, everything was well under control.

Mary Epp's way with people was best illustrated when one of the world's leading playwrights paid a surprise visit to the Bell Clinic. It was a cold, wet spring morning and I was holding my daily lecture and discussion session with our patients. Suddenly the door burst open and a burly, disheveled, rough-looking man bolted in — with one bare foot covered with slush. He glanced around the room for a moment, then sat down at the back and began to listen to my presentation. After a couple of minutes he shouted out, "That's the worst line of bullshit I have ever heard in my life!" This was my introduction to Brendan Behan, who was in Toronto for one of his plays.

Behan continued to rant on and totally disrupted my presentation, which ended abruptly, it being impossible to continue. Alas, one of the other patients present that morning was a clergyman. When Behan spotted him, he began to direct his profanities at the poor fellow, who was totally unable to match the playwright's verbal fireworks. I was having absolutely no success in calming down Behan, so I called in Mary Epp. She was no more disturbed by Behan's behavior than that of any of the other patients. She convinced him to follow her to the kitchen where she sat him down and gave him tea. The great playwright remained perfectly still and quiet while she told him about our philosophy and treatment programs. Mary Epp was the only person to whom he would listen while he was at the Bell Clinic. A few hours later, though, he had had enough and he stormed out of the clinic. But he remained a perfect gentleman all the while Mary Epp was present. Such was her effect on all those with whom she came in contact.

Mary Epp was the head nurse at all our clinics until she retired in 1975. When she died in 1983, we lost not only a wonderful friend but a person who had contributed greatly to whatever clinical successes we had achieved over the years.

In 1958 I received a very pleasant surprise when I was contacted by the Malvern Institute for Alcoholic and Psychiatric studies in Malvern, Pennsylvania. The institute notified me that I had been selected that year to receive their annual Citation of Merit "in recognition of the exemplary leadership and courage he has displayed in furthering the treatment, understanding and welfare of the alcoholic patient, and for many years of outstanding service in this cause." I was invited to receive the honor at a ceremony in Malvern in October that same year.

The event coincided with my first attempt to deal with my own addiction to nicotine. At the time of the ceremony I had not smoked a cigarette in eighteen days. Since I had consistently smoked twenty-five to thirty cigarettes a day for nearly twenty years the sudden nicotine deprivation had a profound effect on my system.

I remember very well the day and time I interrupted my compelling dependence on nicotine with a view to quitting completely: 5:30 P.M. on Friday, October 5, 1958. The withdrawal reaction I experienced over the ensuing weeks was unpleasant and prolonged. I had difficulty concentrating and was depressed and irritable, and Mary finally said to me, "If you ever have to go through this again, let me know in advance so that the children and I can get out of town." To add to my frustration, my mental faculties had also slowed down tremendously. My secretary, Gwen Kavanagh, finally suggested that I stop trying to dictate letters for a couple of weeks, since I wasn't making any sense anyway.

At the presentation at the Malvern Institute that October, however, I felt quite at ease and convinced that I had overcome the more overt symptoms of the withdrawal. One of the physicians attending the ceremony had come from Wilmington, Delaware, and had been a member of the industrial medical staff headed by Dr. George Gehrmann, the original chairman of the Committee on Problem Drinking of the American Association of Industrial Physicians and Surgeons. After I finished my short speech, in which I thanked those responsible for selecting me for the award, he came up to me and asked, "What's happened to you?"

"What do you mean?" I replied.

"For the first time since I've known you," he said, "you spoke slowly enough that even *I* could understand you."

He was highly amused when I explained my withdrawal reaction to nicotine, and said he was pleased that I was beginning to practise what I preached about addiction.

In 1958 the first alcoholism treatment center for Roman Catholic priests in the United States was established at Lake Orion, Michigan, in the former mansion of the Scripps newspaper-publishing family. I was invited to the "Guest House" three or four times annually to conduct three two-hour seminars on the physical, psychological, and social aspects of alcohol addiction. It was a very interesting challenge, and extremely stressful: the priests were exceptionally intelligent and educated and I was forced to field a barrage of questions beyond any I had ever faced before. I cannot recall being more thoroughly exhausted at the end of a day than I was at the end of those seminars, but I gained new insights into their problems and into addiction in general. I was surprised at how frankly the priests discussed their problems, and I learned as much as they did.

I eventually found out that the Guest House approach to treatment and rehabilitation was not universally approved and endorsed by all American bishops. One of them, who believed in a more punitive approach, was put on the same program with me at a conference held in Windsor, Ontario, in the early sixties. I was not a Catholic, and I think the people who ran the Guest House must have decided that it would be most interesting to put the bishop and me together. I felt I had nothing to lose. I told my adversary that I did not agree with his outmoded approach to treating addiction. In the end, the priests seemed quite pleased with the debate, and I enjoyed myself immensely. However, I doubt if the bishop was significantly impressed with my recommendations.

Although the staff at the Bell Clinic and I were gaining more and more insights into the problems of the alcoholic, we still had no overall formula to tie them together. With the stimulation of my various U.S. connections, I particularly wanted to develop such a formula. I remembered how our anatomy professor in medical school had always advised us to draw diagrams so that we could appreciate the relationship of the various organs in any part of the body. He even warned that unless we had a sufficiently accurate mental picture to be able to make such a drawing, we did not know enough to meet his standards. This advice had impressed me, and I had often wondered if we had reached the point of being able to do this with alcohol addiction.

At one point I was experimenting with the design of a number of charts when I received an invitation to address a meeting of the medical staff of General Motors in Chicago in April 1959. I decided to stop fooling around with the various plans, selected the one that seemed to be the best of the lot, and used the occasion to try it out. The paper was published in the *Canadian Medical Association Journal* later that year under the title "Clinical Landmarks to Alcohol Addiction." To facilitate the understanding of alcohol addiction, I had identified three consecutive phases in its progression. The first included the physical, mental, and social factors which initiated a dependence on alcohol in harmful quantities. The second phase covered the physical, mental, and social changes resulting from the process of adaptation to increasingly harmful quantities. The third step was concerned with the cumulative effects of intoxication, malnutrition, and tissue irritation on the physical, mental, and social well-being of the patient.

Although there was nothing startlingly new in my presentation, this blueprint was to have a significant and unexpected effect on our future activities. One of our patients who had attended my presentation of the new chart had recommended to a local film company that my talk be produced as an educational film. I was interested in the idea, but I could see plenty of problems, too. What, for example, would the Ontario College of Physicians and Surgeons think of such an effort? I went for advice to Dr. Joe Dawson, the new registrar-treasurer of the college. I already knew him through several patients who were also medical colleagues. Joe was very encouraging. We decided to go ahead with the film, and we reviewed every word of the introduction to make sure that superlatives were avoided and that no mention was made of the Bell Clinic. The film was eventually released in June 1960, under the title *For Those Who Drink.* Many workers in the addiction field must have been waiting for some kind of blueprint, because the film was soon being shown in all ten Canadian provinces, in every U.S. state, and in several other countries as well. The effort also served our own clinic by sharpening the orientation of our staff members as a team. We all sang different parts, in varying degrees of harmony, but at least we were all trying to sing the same song.

In the late 1950s I became a special lecturer on addiction to the department of pharmacology at the University of Toronto, and I gave a few lectures to the nurses-in-training in several Toronto hospitals. Although the diagrams were useful in helping patients and others visualize the many interrelated problems of the alcohol addict, I felt they left something to be desired as a teaching tool. I believed very strongly at that time in the need for improved methods of teaching about addictions and I knew I had to further fine-tune the blueprint.

I was also concerned about other problems. The trend at that time was to establish psychiatrically oriented clinics to deal with addictions. I addressed this in a paper I presented to the Massachusetts Medical Society in May 1960. Referring to a study that had recently been done in southern California, I pointed out that psychiatrists there were no more interested in the problems of the alcohol addict than were other members of the medical profession, and that only about half of them actually treated alcoholics. Of the percentage that did treat alcoholics, half limited the number of addicts they treated. And the success rates of those who did treat alcoholics were discouraging. Another problem was that even if psychiatrists did or could treat alcoholics, there were simply not enough of them to deal with millions of problem drinkers. And there seemed to be little interest among other medical professionals to accept any responsibility for treating this substantial segment of the population.

In 1959 I had become a regular lecturer with the Utah Summer School of Alcohol Studies in Salt Lake City, which was sponsored by the Mormon Church and which attracted 700 to 800 students at each session. The sessions were held every June, and from 1959 to 1964 I introduced the course with a description of the related factors in alcohol addiction according to our nine-part chart, and then, in another session later that day, explained our three-phase treatment program based on the insights provided by the chart's organization. In turn, I learned that the Mormon Church requires total abstinence from its members, although it seemed to favor our enlightened approach to treatment, rather than a punitive one.

One of the more significant outcomes of the Utah experience was meeting the Reverend Tom Shipp, who was minister of the Lovers' Lane Church in Dallas, Texas. Tom and I became good friends, and soon thereafter I began to receive invitations to put on seminars or workshops for a variety of agencies in the Dallas area. Before long I was participating in the Summer School on Alcoholism, which was held annually in Austin, and conducting special seminars in Houston, Fort Worth, and Waco.

While the various organizations with which I was connected were making inroads in addiction research and treatment programs in the United States, I was pained by the lack of similar progress in Canada. I always looked forward to my adventures in the U.S. because they gave me the opportunity to meet other workers in my field, and to compare ideas about treatment and research. Many of these people were excellent speakers with a great sense of humor. In particular, I enjoyed the speakers from the Yale Center of Alcohol Studies, which had been established in the early 1940s, and those from the National Council of Alcoholism. I met them at almost every conference. At one conference in North Carolina the speaker who was scheduled to talk before me had to bow out at the last minute. He had, however, arranged for an associate to take his place, a North Carolinian with an easy manner and a laconic delivery. He introduced his talk by saying, "I do not pretend to be an expert in the assessment of the results in the treatment of alcoholism. So I rely on the SHAG method. In case y'all don't understand what the SHAG method is, it refers to a 'Scientific Half-Assed Guess'." The definition brought down the house, but it was also quite an accurate term for the methodology used to evaluate addiction treatment in those days.

In 1965 I finally had a blueprint with which I was comfortable. That year I made a presentation at the annual meeting of the Texas Medical Association, in which I discussed our nine-part chart. Following this, the chart was published for the first time in the Texas State *Journal of Medicine* in April of that year. The blueprint formed the basis for the treatment program we had developed, and which we would continue to follow during our years at the Donwood Institute.

I successfully presented the chart on many subsequent occasions and became increasingly satisfied with its reception by a wide variety of audiences. I began to refer to the physical, mental, and social predisposing factors as areas 1, 2, and 3; the physical, mental, and social changes from the primary process of adaptation as areas 4, 5, and 6; and the physical, mental, and social changes from intoxication, malnutrition, and tissue irritation as areas 7, 8, and 9. The numbering system helped simplify the chart, once the areas were defined.

My own addiction to tobacco was not as easily explained as the chart was, and my battle to end my smoking habit continued off and on for several years. I once managed to stop smoking for fifteen months and was just beginning to feel comfortable with my abstinent state when the figurative roof caved in. In January 1960, there was a

Controlled Desire	Uncontrolled Desire	Secondary Consequences
Predisposing Factors	Adaptation to Harmful Quantities	Intoxication and Malnutrition
Initial Physical State	Acquired Tolerance and Withdrawal	Physical Changes
1. **Direct Factors** — Natural tolerance. Ability to enjoy alcohol in harmful quantities. **Indirect:** Chronic illness, injury or disfigurement affecting mental state.	4. Overactivity and acquired desire from physical adaptation to depressants **when drinking:** restlessness insomnia poor appetite loss of control **on withdrawal:** "shakes" hallucinations convulsions	7. Reduced tolerance Blackouts Neurological changes Disorders in the liver, stomach, pancreas Bruises, lacerations, burns, and fractures Proneness to infection
Initial Mental State	Habituation and Defensive Thinking	Mental Changes
2. Sustained desire or willingness to use alcohol in harmful quantities — relief of: anxiety frustration depression boredom loneliness — increase of pleasure — pressure to conform	5. Acquired desire from mental adaptation plus awareness of trouble alibis lying cover-up resentment suspicion projection, etc.	8. Reaction to chronic intoxication: mental dulling irrationality poor concentration poor emotional control Reaction to social breakdown: shame guilt remorse despair
Initial Social State	Manipulation	Social Changes
3. **Indirect Factors** — Chronic problems in family, work, etc., affecting mental state. **Direct Factors** — Ability to obtain alcohol in harmful quantities. Money, supply, social customs, etc.	6. Manipulation of family, work and community situations to accommodate increasing desire solitary drinking hiding supply "coffee" breaks working late visiting sick walking dog etc.	9. Home: strain separation divorce Occupation: poor efficiency absenteeism loss of job Community: impaired driving assault theft

NINE-PART CHART FOR ALCOHOL DEPENDENCE

severe ice storm in our area, which resulted in broken power lines and blackouts. Our home was one of those affected, so I sent Mary and the children to the Lampings', whose house had not lost its electricity. I stayed home to operate a gasoline-powered sump pump to keep our cellar from flooding. I was feeling very sorry for myself at about 3:00 A.M. when I discovered a packet of cigarettes that I had received as a Christmas gift, and had tossed into the rack of the refrigerator door. In a flash of total insanity the idea leaped at me: "You're all alone, the house is cold, so why not have one?" And I did. I was "hooked" again, and I continued to smoke for the next two years and three months before trying to stop one more time.

Now that we had the chart to consider the possible relationships encountered with addiction problems, I began to isolate the forces contributing to alcoholics' resistance to treatment. This led to the eventual publication, in January 1965, of my paper, "Defensive Thinking in Alcohol Addicts" in the *CMAJ.* There were more requests for reprints of this article than for all my other papers combined. In it I discussed the reasons why it is often so difficult for professionals to successfully bridge the gap between beginning treatment and a rehabilitation program for the addict.

Addicts have an initial compelling desire for harmful quantities of the addicting substance, plus the acquired uncontrolled desire that arises from mental and physical adaptation to those quantities. They are caught in the grip of these powerful forces, which compel them to continue to sustain and expand their addiction in spite of their awareness of progressively serious consequences to their health. It also puts them on the defensive, which means that consequently they resist treatment, an attitude that forms an integral part of their disability.

Over the years we found that this defensive thinking leads addicts to rationalize, to lie, to project, to be resentful and suspicious, to make heroic efforts to protect their sources of supply, to drink or take drugs alone, to show remorse and moodiness, to become frustrated, and to develop progressively greater difficulties in communicating with colleagues at work, family, and friends. The paper was aimed at assisting physicians to interrupt the addict's defensive thinking sufficiently to initiate a treatment and rehabilitation program. But doctors had to take the time and trouble to identify the primary and secondary factors in the case of each patient as outlined in the nine-part chart.

When asked to address outside groups on the subject of addiction, I used the chart to illustrate the components in the addictive process and stressed the need to understand the nature of addiction before it could be defeated. I also emphasized the importance of replacing arbitrary moralistic attitudes commonly associated with addiction with understanding, support, and the expectation of successful intervention and treatment.

To the extent that the medical profession came into contact with the addict, the doctors were usually concerned with the medical and surgical problems in area 7, less frequently with the withdrawal reactions of area 4, and only occasionally with the predisposing physical problems in area 1. They rarely showed much knowledge of, or interest in, the other six areas, particularly in the addictive changes in areas 4, 5, and 6 as an important and treatable phase of addiction. Many doctors today continue to treat liver disease and the other medical or surgical consequences of addiction without attempting to interrupt, reduce, and eventually inactivate the underlying addiction itself. To me, this is comparable to amputating a gangrenous toe without treating the patient's primary diabetes.

Most of the psychiatrists I knew persisted in focusing their attention on area 2 — the predisposing psychological situation — and many of them believed that correcting the problems in this area would be sufficient. They persisted in believing that heavy drinking, which may initially have been a reaction to a psychological problem, remained that, even years later. Many failed to appreciate that patients could become locked into a pathological drinking pattern by the process of habituation alone, plus the cumulative effect of chronic intoxication with depressants. These were the additional factors in the mental state of the alcohol addict referred to in areas 5 and 8. I was appalled to overhear a psychoanalyst say, "Given enough time on the couch, any alcoholic patient should be able to return to a safe drinking pattern."

I recall a patient who had come to our clinic from the United States years before. He lived in a large city that had unusually good medical and psychiatric facilities. He had taken his drinking problem to a well-known analyst, who I believed had started off on the right foot by insisting that the man get sober and stay sober before he would take him as a patient. The patient co-operated completely and remained sober for many months, until the psychiatrist finally told him that he need not come back any longer for treatment. According to the psychiatrist, the man had gradually worked through his conflicts and ought then to be able to safely resume moderate drinking. The man took the therapist's advice and went on the damnest wingding he ever had. When his family brought him to us, he was violently ill and confused. After his shakes had settled sufficiently we had a chat.

"What the hell happened?" he asked. "I was supposed to be cured." Before I could answer that, I had to ask him a few questions.

"Had you come to believe that your uncontrolled drinking was caused by subconscious conflicts going back to childhood?"

"Yes."

"How old were you when you started to drink?"

"Sixteen," he replied.

"Did these childhood experiences begin before you were sixteen?"

"Yes."

"Did you always drink in this uncontrolled way from the time you started drinking?" I asked.

"No," he responded, "I used to get drunk pretty often, but I had no trouble stopping."

"When did you find you first had trouble stopping?"

"About age twenty-six."

"From that time on, did it get more difficult to stop when you wanted to?"

"Yes."

"In my opinion," I said, "your recent bout has little to do with your childhood experiences, although I do think they were related to your tendency to get drunk repeatedly as a teenager. You got drunk and stayed drunk because you have developed the physical and mental characteristics of addiction to alcohol. Unfortunately, these changes are not completely reversible with present medical knowledge, and all of the psychiatry in the world can't guarantee you a return to safe, controlled drinking. I believe that you now have no alternative but to learn how to live without alcohol for the rest of your life."

The man took my advice, and to the best of my knowledge stayed far away from booze after that relapse.

Unlike psychiatrists, sociologists tend to concentrate on area 3, the social factors of economic status, the availability of alcohol, and the drinking customs of their particular culture and community. Social workers are primarily interested in the indirect social factors in area 3 — the social situations to which the drinker reacts with uncomfortable tension. They are also interested in the social changes of areas 6 and 9 — an interest they share with the police, lawyers, the courts, the clergy, and just about everyone else in the community. The area-9 problems with alcohol and drug addiction are the undesirable consequences that give addiction its social stigma. Since there are no comparable area-9 problems related to an addiction to food or tobacco, the police are rarely involved. (Of course, the situation is changing today with tobacco, as smoking becomes more socially unacceptable.)

The social consequences of alcohol and drug addiction — the part of the addict's problem that makes the headlines and involves the courts, employers, family, and other members of the person's community — are the most significant parts of the whole disorder. These area-9 problems are continuously processed through the legal system, just as area-7 problems are repeatedly processed through the hospitals.

In August 1966, I presented a paper to the annual meeting of the American Bar Association. I discussed some of the medico-legal implications of addiction, dealing particularly with social consequences. This was my first attempt to use the blueprint to present the subject of addiction to the legal profession. The paper was called "Addiction, Alcoholism, and Freedom of Will." The thrust of the speech underlined the fact that the primary disability in addiction is an uncontrolled desire. This fact had to be recognized by anyone designing or undertaking treatment programs or considering new legislation. I told those at the meeting that addiction combines an abnormal desire with the physical, mental, and social problems that precede it and others resulting from it. The primary objective of both the legal and medical professions should be to inactivate this pathological desire.

It simply does not make sense to deal endlessly with the consequences of addiction, I argued in my talk, without exploring a more effective approach to inactivating the addiction itself. The person being charged with impaired driving for the second or third time is demonstrating an unhealthy dependence on a depressant that will not be corrected by fines or jail. The addict is swept along like a weak swimmer in an ever-stronger current. The widely held belief that it is necessary to wait until he asks for help himself simply results in unnecessary and severe damage from intoxication and malnutrition. Death rather than treatment is frequently the result. I stressed the need for new and improved treatment techniques, and asked the legal profession to consider collaborating with other groups to develop and improve legislation to provide effective, humane legal barriers to the unchecked progress of addiction.

The speech was well received, and it illustrated for me the wide applicability of the nine-part chart. The chart made it so much easier for us in the field to explain the problems of addiction and how to treat them to people in all areas of life. And it revealed the areas in which people in the community can play a significant role in helping the addict overcome his or her problem.

People often ask me if I had any statistical proof in those days to indicate that our programs were indeed working. During the Bell Clinic period, whenever our meager finances permitted, we retained students and once a physician to assess our results one year after admission. These were the first tests to assure us that fifty percent or more of our patients had maintained unbroken abstinence for one year, or had had brief relapses, which reinforced their commitment to a sober, healthier life. These were the ones who had to try it one more time just to make sure they could not control their drinking. As soon as possible after Donwood began operations, we undertook more scientific studies, which confirmed the earlier Bell Clinic results.

CHAPTER ELEVEN

Laying a New Foundation

On December 31, 1957, our fifth and last child, Brian, was born, rounding out our family. It was the happy end to what had been a good year. The Bell Clinic had settled down, we were meeting our costs, paying off our debts, and for the first time ever, we even had a bit left over. The patient load had stabilized at near-capacity, Mary had turned over most of her responsibilities at the clinic to a professional business manager, and an excellent cook had arrived to pamper staff and patients alike. I began to contemplate our next move.

A few friends and advisors, particularly Ken Ferguson, had begun to point out that the Bell Clinic was too dependent on my personal attention to survive without me. Staff, family, and friends also felt that our hard-won progress could somehow be protected and developed by operating on a larger scale. The idea was an attractive one, but I was hesitant to act on it. We were just beginning to experience a little peace and security. Would this mean a return to turmoil? I did not think so, because I had the naive idea that I had been on the firing-line long enough to be able to anticipate most of the difficulties that might arise in a new project.

Ken Ferguson and I discussed various possibilities at considerable length. I had been a member of the Professional Advisory Board of the Addiction Research Foundation of Ontario for three years, which at that time was under Ken's chairmanship. The foundation itself had given Ken an idea. He was chatting with me one evening, when he surprised me by asking, "Have you ever thought of establishing a foundation yourself and carrying on on a non-profit basis?" He believed a privately organized foundation in the addiction field could serve a useful purpose, similar to those organized to deal with other medical problems, like cancer and cardiovascular disease. Such a foundation could provide an opportunity for a concerned public to support work in addiction and complement the work of government foundations, like ARF, which were wholly dependent on provincial funds.

Ken also suggested that our treatment orientation and methods should be incorporated into a larger, more stable operation than could be provided by our small private clinic. I knew of so many clinics and information centers for alcoholics in both Canada and the United States that had either failed or remained relatively ineffective that I was determined not to rush into this new venture. We would require more than our personal experience with addiction to become firmly rooted in business, government, and academic circles. As it turned out, I need not have had any concern about rushing into anything; there were enough obstacles in our path already before our plans could materialize.

No planning for any kind of hospital or medical foundation in Ontario was possible without the support of Dr. Matthew Dymond, then minister of health for the province, and Dr. Ian Urquhart, then chairman of the newly organized Hospital Services Commission. The commission had assumed responsibility for general hospital care in Ontario in January 1959. The officials at the Ministry of Health were initially unenthusiastic when they received our proposal to expand our services. They were just in the process of organizing psychiatric units in many general hospitals throughout the province, and were moving away from the idea of licensing hospitals that provided only special services, such as the treatment of addictions.

My first discussions with Dr. Urquhart had been discouraging. He quickly convinced me that no amount of eloquence on my part was going to stampede him into any quick change of policy. The commission's policy at the early stage was to pay none of the hospital costs for the treatment of alcohol addiction. They were already up to their ears with the problems of introducing the new hospital-insurance plan to the general hospitals throughout the province. In that sense it was a particularly inopportune time for me to broach the subject of hospital insurance for the treatment of alcoholism.

Since alcoholics in Ontario represented a potential patient load of about 100,000, for which neither funds nor facilities had been allocated, it was easy to understand why the commission was cautious about assessing my request to consider insuring this group. In addition to some assurance that alcoholics would eventually receive insurance coverage under the government plan comparable to that for patients afflicted by any other type of disability, we also required the commission's approval to allow us to build any kind of hospital, public or private. In spite of all their other problems during their hectic first year of operation, the commission sent a team to examine every detail of our clinical program — orientation, philosophy, fee structure, salaries, employee benefits, and the like. They must have been satisfied because from that point on we made slow but steady progress. The commission began to cover part of the hospital costs at the Bell Clinic that very year.

From the onset of our discussions, Dr. Urquhart had recommended that our best chance to expand was to plan a special public hospital, which would have qualified us for both federal and provincial grants to help defray the costs of construction, and most of the operating costs thereafter. I was afraid that this would mean that we would be involved in an endless succession of bureaucratic obstacles, which could interfere with our plans and long-term goals. I suspected that we might end up treating mainly indigents while the government ran the whole show. My experience at the Bell and Alex G. Brown clinics had led me to believe that the two patient groups responded best to different facilities and programs designed for their special needs.

Accordingly, I preferred to risk trying to raise all the money solely by private means at first. Although an approved private hospital would have a significant portion of its medical costs covered by the government insurance plan, there would still be a portion of the bill that the patient would have to pay. Frankly, I favored such a plan, since I felt that many patients would be more inclined to appreciate a service which they had to pay for (at least in part) themselves. Dr. Urquhart pointed out that the days of private hospitals in Canada were numbered and that my fears about operating a public institution were unfounded. I stubbornly stuck to my guns, however, and thus made my first serious mistake with the project.

In 1959 the Ministry of Health and the Ontario Hospital Services Commission actually approved our plans to proceed with what became the Donwood project — a special, private hospital for both alcohol and drug addicts, since drug addiction was obviously on the increase. In September, Gwen Kavanagh, who had previously been hired as my private secretary, became secretary of the new institute as well. Her warmth, competence, and practical knowledge of the outside world provided a much-needed bridge between our tiny island and the important people whose support we required. Her prior experience working with business executives was crucial to our success in enlisting the support of corporations and individuals for planning, designing, financing, and operating the Donwood Institute. In December 1959 we obtained our charter to "establish and operate a hospital and clinic for the treatment and rehabilitation of alcohol, drug, and other addicts, and to conduct research into the problems of addiction in all its forms."

Most of 1960 was taken up in a search for suitably eminent people to serve on our founding board of directors. Gwen understood the kind of people we required for the board and knew how to contact them, skills that were vital throughout the seven years and three months between obtaining our charter and opening the doors to the first patients at Donwood. Many businesspeople at first appeared interested in our plans, until they found out the kind of illness we would be treating. Then they usually told me that they had no time for additional community projects. But by November, seven people had joined the board and we had begun to plant roots in the business community. Mitchell Sharp, then vice-president of the Brazilian Traction Company, became our first chairman, and he held the position until 1963 when he resigned to join the Liberal Party and enter federal politics. He subsequently held a succession of cabinet posts, including minister of external affairs. J. Donald Bell (not related), a Toronto lawyer, became vice-chairman. The society had set up a committee involving both of us to consider more effective legislation to deal with those addicts most resistant to treatment. On one occasion, as we were about to present our report to the society's executive, a legal wit introduced us with the statement, "We will now hear the case of Bell and Bell versus Haig and Haig!"

In April 1961 we purchased a six-acre property in Vaughan Township just outside Metropolitan Toronto — far enough from the city to eventually cause serious trouble for us. The location, by the Don River in a well-treed area, provided us with the innocuous-sounding name of the Donwood Institute. A patient donated the down payment of $10,000 for the land and the Royal Bank loaned us $20,000 more to close the deal. Our usual concern over water supply and sewage disposal was not great enough for it to be considered a problem at the time. Given our history of involvement with sewer systems to that point, I should have known better.

The rest of the year was taken up primarily with fund-raising. Our architects, John. B. Parkin Associates, had estimated a total cost of about $1,500,000 to complete the hospital. So we hired a professional fund-raiser who divided the campaign into two parts — former patients who could be approached only by me personally (since their identities had to be protected) and people in the business community who would be contacted by the board's directors and their associates. Three top executives from the business community were added to the board of directors to give us additional status in that area.

In the meantime I was becoming more and more disgusted with myself for my own smoking addiction. In April 1962 I finally interrupted my nicotine dependence again, this time for keeps. I had been borrowing the occasional cigarette from packs our patients had left in their rooms and flushing the used butts down the toilet. One day Mary caught me smoking behind the furnace. I consistently demonstrated the full range of manipulation, rationalization, and cover-up tactics that characterized the behavior of my addicted patients.

I burned the last of my cigarettes in the fireplace on the day I quit for good, but I was so furious with myself that I neglected to close the flap on a three-layer packet of matches. The packet immediately caught fire and seared the palm of my hand, and the incident became a painful reminder of my renewed determination to kick the habit. For some weeks Mary had anticipated that I was working myself up again to quitting, and she had prudently taken our two youngest children to Florida for a vacation. I followed with the three oldest children a few days later, burned hand and all, and spent most of the time there sleeping. But my sleep was not always restful. Nearly ten years passed before I finally stopped having horrible dreams about relapsing.

Even while continuing to run the Bell Clinic and plan the Donwood project, I found the time to travel to addiction and other health-care conferences around North America. Usually no one greeted me at the airport when I came back to Toronto, so upon returning from a speaking engagement in Calgary in August 1962, I was surprised to find Mary standing at the arrivals area. She brought terrible news about my sister, Jean. The day before, a driver had lost control of his truck, crossed the median, and crashed into Jean's little car on the driver's side. She had been killed instantly.

Jean and I had both lived in the Toronto area, and we were very close. She was warm, stable, and a great source of strength to me. While I was planning the Donwood project, I often thought of how much Jean, who had trained as a nurse and also worked as a nursing administrator, could contribute to the new clinic. But I knew that she was a confirmed housewife and that this was only a dream.

I had lost both a very close friend and a valued consultant, whose advice I had sought through the years. Mary had lost one of her closest friends, and our children had lost a very special person in their lives. I did not realize how important she was in my life until she was no longer there.

It took some time for me to get over the shock of Jean's death and to refocus my efforts on the Donwood project. I can thank some former patients for helping me to rekindle my interest. In 1963 they came through handsomely with contributions of about $175,000. The Honorable Leslie Frost, a former premier of Ontario, agreed that spring to be honorary chairman of the fund-raising drive, and we were underway. By June, donations amounted to about $500,000, and enthusiasm and morale were high. John B. Parkin replaced Mitchell Sharp as chairman of the board of directors, and Ken Ferguson became vice-chairman.

Disaster of another kind struck that October. The final

consultants' reports on water and sewers strongly advised against proceeding with plans for a hospital on our chosen site. Every effort to develop adequate facilities on the property, or to obtain them from neighboring municipalities, had failed. The fund-raising drive had to be halted. Not only was the location unsuitable, but I had finally become convinced that we should follow the original advice of the commission: abandon plans for a private hospital and reroute our thinking in the direction of a special public hospital.

I had finally realized that this move to a public hospital was imperative for more reasons than qualifying for government grants toward the cost of construction. It had become clear to me that one of the important objectives of the Donwood Institute should be to explore means of integrating the treatment of addiction more effectively into the mainstream of clinical and community life. All communities accepted public hospitals. By working out the problems of financing and operating a special public hospital for addiction treatment, we hoped to move toward the integration of such treatment into the existing hospital facilities in any community. As a private hospital, this kind of co-operative effort with public facilities would have been difficult. I had almost made the serious mistake of organizing another isolated clinical island. Naturally, it became necessary for me to advise all our donors of these major changes in our plans, and I could only hope that it would be unnecessary to refund their donations on the basis of an altered application. The rest of the year was spent in a futile search for another property.

After tramping through the countryside with our architect, Jack Owen, a member of the Parkin firm, and Ken Ferguson, we finally found a location that seemed suitable. When I asked the owner about sewers, he promptly replied that there would be no problem, no problem at all. Since we were well beyond the city limits I asked him how he could be so sure.

"Do you see that field down by the road where you came in?" he asked. "Well, that's where the new sewage disposal plant will be built. You can't miss."

"Can't miss" was right, I thought — can't miss being associated with sewage disposal for the rest of our lives. I seemed to be in constant trouble with sewers, and I could see that it wasn't over yet. From always being too far away from them, we were now much too close.

Early in 1964, about a month or so later, Dr. John Nielsen, the new chairman of the Hospital Services Commission, suggested that property might be available from the federal Department of Veterans Affairs, close to the Sunnybrook Medical Centre. Not only was he correct, but unbelievably, everything about the new location was superior to anything we had seen before. We purchased it in May from the Crown Assets Disposal Corporation in Ottawa. Happily, since it was also located by the Don River, we were able to keep the Donwood name. The town of Leaside agreed to sell us water — we were actually *handy* to sewers — and the architects were instructed to start on the new plans.

Although the property was ideally located from the standpoint of convenience and attractiveness of setting, it had one drawback: the only possibility of future expansion was toward the Divadale property to the west, still owned by the Department of Veterans Affairs. In May 1964, I wrote to the minister of veterans affairs, Roger Taillet, outlining our position and possible need to expand in the future. I requested that Donwood be granted first refusal when and if the property became available. In spite of the department's acknowledgment of my request, the Divadale property was turned over to the University of Toronto two years later, along with the entire Sunnybrook property. It was fourteen years later before Donwood finally acquired seven acres of the Divadale property from the University of Toronto for $800,000 — half of which was paid by the Ministry of Health.

By this time I was quite nervous about any new project, and my agitation, reflecting an accumulation of the years of effort, was beginning to show. During a public meeting with our Leaside neighbors a man stood up and yelled, "Do you realize that these people plan to build an asylum at our very doorstep?" According to Jack Owen, I exploded so suddenly and violently that I landed several feet in front of my chair.

"It's obvious to me," I responded immediately, "that you have serious misconceptions about the kind of patients who would come to Donwood. They are the same kind of people who live on your street, work with you, and are members of your family. You can be very sure of one thing: there will be less drinking at the Donwood address than at most other addresses in Leaside!" To the credit of the Leasiders, they did not try to oppose us further in any way, and they continued to take a friendly interest in our activities.

The new architectural plans were ready in March 1965, but we did not have enough money to proceed, even with government grants. The fund-raising drive had long since come to a complete halt, and I could see trouble trying to revive it. Finally, in June, I broke down. Every task, no matter how small, had become an effort. I found no joy in my work, or in anything else. To borrow a phrase from Dr. Ruth Fox, a physician in New York, I felt as if I were "walking through sand up to my knees." Bill Hall promptly diagnosed "battle fatigue" after more than five years of pursuing my project, and he had me admitted to St. Michael's Hospital for a thorough examination. Then he insisted that I take a three-month rest.

I spent those three months at a small cottage we rented at Turkey Point on Lake Erie. Mary, unfortunately, had to stay at home to run the Bell Clinic. The two eldest children, Jan and Ronnie, were in university and had already taken summer jobs. So we decided that the next in line, Linda, who was then eighteen, should come along to look after me while I recuperated. The rest of the family would come down on weekends to visit whenever possible.

Linda and I became much closer during this period. She was lively and positive, and we talked a great deal. We bought an old car and an inboard motorboat to get out and enjoy the surroundings, and I gradually began to recover my stress tolerance. Later in the course of that invigorating summer I was able to map out my strategy for getting Donwood off the ground. I also began to realize just how lucky I had been. Many people in my position would have suffered far more severe, even life-threatening complications from the stress I had faced.

I had actually cracked up on the very day that I was supposed to have left for my regular introductory presentation at the Utah Summer School of Alcohol Studies. During the summer months I asked myself if it was possible that the United States could somehow survive without my personal attention. The answer was obvious. I began to decline most of the invitations I received to participate in outside programs or projects, and I had to admit I was impressed by how well the Americans got along without my contribution.

My convalescence allowed me the first extended break I had had from my work since 1946. Before returning to Toronto at the end of the summer, I made a further major decision: to go back to the Ministry of Health and the Hospital Services Commission and request additional funds of about $600,000. At that time Jack Jamieson was in charge of all grants to hospitals in Ontario on behalf of the commission, and when I returned I got an appointment with him. I also arranged for George L. Holmes, then chairman of the board of the Manufacturers Life Insurance Company and of the Donwood Institute, and Ken Ferguson to accompany me. I sensed that neither of them was optimistic that I would succeed in my request. I was delighted when Jack Jamieson arranged for a grant to cover half of our needs and a loan at three percent for the other half, on the condition that Donwood also be prepared to engage in teaching and research.

Our fortunes were changing dramatically for the better. Late on a Friday afternoon that fall I had a telephone call from an officer from one of the trust companies in downtown Toronto. Assuming it was another call requesting an admission over the weekend, I accepted it rather gruffly. To my amazement, the caller wanted to inform me that I had been left a considerable amount of money in a will. Over a decade earlier, during the Shadow Brook period, I had treated a businessman from Toronto who had continued to be actively involved in the Three Point Club, the continuing-therapy component at Shadow Brook. I recalled that he had no children of his own; he had taken quite an interest in my kids and family activities, and he occasionally voiced some concern about our financial situation. Our contact had been very occasional since the Shadow Brook operation had closed down. So I was completely dumbfounded when the Bell family found itself the grateful recipients of a very handsome bequest of $60,000.

When I told Mary the news, we agreed to buy a house, one that had to have ample grounds for gardening, which during the past twenty years has expanded to become an important part of my life and a rewarding break from the problems of other people. Mary found the right house in North York in the northern part of Metropolitan Toronto. We also had sufficient funds to be able to completely remodel the basement for the accommodation and entertainment of family, grandchildren, and friends — all without a mortgage. In 1966 we obtained a line of credit for Donwood from the Royal Bank for up to $350,000 and began to search for more staff. As I watched the steel beams being hoisted into place at last, I sometimes found it difficult to believe that the project was actually coming to life. Meanwhile, the daily operations at the Bell Clinic continued.

In April a well-known member of a prominent American

family was admitted to the Bell Clinic for treatment. William Clay Ford, a grandson of Henry Ford, had developed a problem with alcohol, which had progressed to the point that the family and physicians at the Ford Hospital in Detroit were seriously concerned. A special committee had been set up to explore alternative treatment centers, and I was pleased when they chose the Bell Clinic.

Bill had married Martha Firestone, the daughter of Harvey S. Firestone, Jr., of tire fame, and they had four children, three daughters and a son. Martha came to Willowdale with Bill and stayed in a neighboring house while Bill was being treated in the clinic. Bill eventually made a complete recovery and has maintained sobriety for twenty-two years. Our chance contact with him dramatically influenced the future of our work, and deepened our connection with the United States.

When Bill entered the Bell Clinic for treatment, plans were already well advanced for the Donwood Institute, and he and Martha became very interested in the prospect of an enlarged operation based on our program. The following winter, in 1967, I traveled to Detroit to ask him if he would consider becoming a founding member of the board of directors for the Donwood Institute. He agreed, and was one of the speakers at our official opening in June of 1967.

The Donwood Institute celebrated Canada's centennial year by launching operations at its new hospital. Construction was finished by January, and in February the furnishings and decorating were done. The four floors of the L-shaped building overlooked a wooded ravine. The reddish-brown structure, driveway, flowerbeds, and parking area had all been fitted into a carefully preserved grove of maples and pines. The brick decor and oak paneling framed rooms carpeted in a warm orange-red. The lounge, dining-room, common rooms, and most of the bedrooms with their spacious windows, opened onto a view of the ravine. Every patient, rich or poor, had his or her own room, some with private baths and some shared. Panels of cheerful colors along the halls harmonized with the furnishings in adjacent rooms. Thanks to our decision to allow the architects to supervise the decoration and selection of the furniture, the atmosphere was in harmony with the building and the setting. The nine-bed admitting unit was the only part that looked like a hospital, and it was fully equipped to cope with any diagnostic or therapeutic situation we were likely to encounter. Some of the early patients dubbed the admitting unit "Happy Valley" — a name that has been used ever since we stopped admissions to the Bell Clinic in February and received our first patients in the new hospital in March. Within a few weeks the commission extended the same insurance coverage to our patients as was available to patients across the province for the treatment of any other illness.

Dr. Dymond was the guest of honor and special speaker at our official opening in June. He summarized our development and thanked all those who had assisted in planning and in meeting the financial costs. He was followed by Ken Ferguson and Bill Ford, and then I gave my own short address. I described the kind of clinic we had set out to create — a warm, non-threatening place that would be an orientation center for patients and for their families for as long as necessary. It was to be a hospital in which light, color, flowers, music, and beauty in many forms would be enjoyed in an atmosphere of human warmth and understanding. It was a difficult speech for me to give, not only because of the emotions brought on by the occasion, but also because I suspected it would be Ward Smith's last public appearance. He died of lung cancer less than three weeks later. Although Ward and I did not have much occasion to work closely together after the alco-dial research, he had remained a close friend and confidant.

In the meantime we continued to search for new staff members to add to the nucleus of our former Bell Clinic staff, which was headed by Mary Epp. My old high-school chum, Dr. George Birtch, was retained as our new director of the continuing-therapy program. I had had my eye on George for many years as I followed his progress in the United Church ministry, and I considered his special qualifications ideal for the job I had in mind.

Bill Ford remained on the board of directors at Donwood for several years, and the William and Martha Ford Fund eventually contributed about a half-million dollars to support research and evaluation studies in the years ahead, at a time when there was no possibility of our acquiring comparable funding from any agency in Canada. Bill had a great sense of humor. The Royal Bank had supported us at the Bell Clinic since 1956, and John Coleman, a vice-president of the bank in the early 1960s, had become chairman of our board. This meant that we held several of the meetings in the boardroom of the Royal Bank in downtown Toronto. The first time Bill walked into the well-appointed room he looked around and said, "Doctor, if we don't watch out we'll end up making this business respectable."

In June of 1967, three months after we began treating patients at Donwood, arrangements were made to have Harvey Firestone, Jr., Martha Ford's father, admitted to the clinic. A friend and physician for the Firestone family, Dr. Jean Purdue, had flown from Miami Beach to Akron, Ohio, to help convince Mr. Firestone to enter Donwood for treatment. I flew down to Akron and met her at the Firestone home, where we prepared him for the trip. By that point he was very frail and had multiple complicating disabilities. I flew back with him in the company jet and we began treatment immediately.

Harvey Firestone presented us with a much more difficult and complicated assortment of clinical problems than his son-in-law, Bill, had the previous year. He was sixty-seven years old, and we realized soon after his arrival that the usual period of four to seven weeks of initial treatment would be far too short to help him effectively. It wasn't until September that he began to show significant improvement in general health. It was marked by the renewed lively interest he took in his personal affairs back home, and the comparable interest he showed in Donwood's activities and operation. When he was well enough he became the one asking the questions: "How did you think up this concept? Who helped you build it? Where did you get the money?" He became very interested in applying the Donwood approach to treatment in the United States.

As Mr. Firestone continued to recover I found him to be a very gifted individual. He had the remarkable capacity to mask his emotions with the most effective poker face of anyone I had ever known. As we became better acquainted, I realized that if I wanted to know what he was feeling, I had to watch his eyes very carefully, because they were the only indicator of his emotions. This faculty must have stood him in good stead during many stressful board meetings and business transactions during his career.

The Donwood Institute was too large to permit my personal involvement with the patients, as had been the case in all the clinics that preceded it. Since Mr. Firestone insisted on discussing his problems with me personally, he provided me with a welcome opportunity to renew the type of close relationship that my patients and I had taken for granted in the past.

Harvey Firestone remained at Donwood for six months, until December 1967, and by that time he knew more about the details of planning our clinic — its financing, management, and problems — than anyone on our board of directors, with the possible exception of Ken Ferguson. Shortly before he left, he reiterated that he wanted to try to get something similar established in the United States. I was pleased to hear this, particularly when his secretary, Bernice Vigar, added, "You are the first new friend that Mr. Firestone has made in many years."

Harvey Firestone, Jr., had been responsible for expanding the Firestone Tire and Rubber Company from a North American to an international organization. It had been his task to locate a place to establish a rubber plantation, which would provide Firestone with a new source of raw material. He finally selected Liberia, on the west coast of Africa, a country founded in the nineteenth century for former American slaves. In one of the discussions I had with him while he was a patient, I mentioned that I hoped some day to have the chance to visit Africa myself. Shortly before he left Donwood, he said to me, "Well, when will you and your wife be ready to go?"

"Go where?" I asked, puzzled.

"I thought you said you wanted to go to Africa," he replied.

I had almost forgotten our conversation, and I said hesitantly, "Well . . . yes . . . I guess I did say that."

"Well," he continued, "when do you want to go? I have it all set up for you."

And indeed he had. In February 1968, Mary and I flew to New York, where we stayed in his private suite at the Waldorf Towers for a night. The following day we flew first-class to Dakar in North Africa, where we changed planes and flew to Monrovia, the capital of Liberia. For the next two weeks we were the guests of the Firestone Company, which at that time operated the largest rubber plantation in the world. The entire trip was a gift.

The long-time leader of Liberia in 1968 was President William Tubman, who had become a friend of Harvey Firestone forty years earlier when the latter had negotiated with the Liberian government for the establishment of the rubber plantation. As a special feature of our vacation, Mr. Firestone had arranged for Mary and me to attend a special luncheon in the president's palace. Most of the other guests at the luncheon were, as far as we could tell, relatives of President Tubman, who seemed to have a rather large family. The meal lasted from one o'clock to about five o'clock, and included a great many courses with a different wine served with each.

After our visit to Liberia, Mary and I stopped off on the way home to visit the Canary Islands. Soon after Mary and I arrived on Gran Canaria and checked into our hotel, we had a visitor, who introduced himself as the representative of the Firestone Corporation on the Canary Islands. He had been informed of our visit by Mr. Firestone, and had brought his Mercedes to the hotel for our use while we were there, along with an attractive young woman who acted as our interpreter. This was typical of the thoughtfulness exhibited by Mr. Firestone during the years that I knew him.

By June of 1968, Harvey Firestone succeeded in founding the Donwood Foundation of America, a name that was subsequently changed to the American Association Against Addiction, after U.S. Treasury officials began to crack down on suspected tax privileges being taken by other so-called charitable foundations. Dr. Jean Purdue was named founding president, and I was named chief consultant. The foundation's main purpose was to broaden support for the Donwood Institute in Canada and facilitate the adaptation of Donwood's methods in the United States. Other board members included Pierre Heftler, the lawyer for Bill and Martha Ford, and Bernie Frazier, who was in charge of public relations for the Firestone Tire and Rubber Company. Bernice Vigar, Harvey Firestone's personal secretary, became secretary for the foundation.

Another important assignment drew me to the United States in September of that year — my role as co-chairman, with Dr. Ebbe Hoff of Virginia, of the section on medical treatment for the International Congress on Alcoholism, which was held in Washington, D.C. Mary and I decided to drive down to the conference, and we stayed overnight at the Firestone home in Akron. When we arose the next morning and met Harvey at breakfast, I could tell by the expression in his eyes that something significant had happened. He looked very sad, and said, "My man gave me a very bad report this morning. He examined the tires on your car and found one Uniroyal, one Goodyear, and two Goodrichs — most of them in a very sorry state of repair."

I did not know quite how to react to this. Harvey smoothly added that he had not waited for my approval but had instructed his man to take our car and have it completely outfitted with four of the best Firestone tires. At this point his eyes began to twinkle, although he continued to display the saddest expression. In his own inimitable fashion Harvey had presented me with a *fait accompli* and had enjoyed himself immensely in the process.

The year ended on a high note. We received the remainder of the government grants for Donwood in November. This enabled us to pay off our loan to the Royal Bank and to retire every other outstanding debt, with the exception of the three-percent loan of $160,000 to the Ontario government. Our patients — those "hopeless characters" nobody wanted — had contributed more than a half-million dollars by themselves, almost a third of the total.

CHAPTER TWELVE

Donwood

When the Donwood Institute began operations in March 1967, the Ministry of Health would pay for only twenty-eight days of in-patient care in any hospital. Since ours was a long-term facility, I simply crammed as much treatment as possible for each patient into the twenty-eight days and the rest was done later. Some American centers adopted the twenty-eight-day approach on the assumption that it was based on clinical judgment, without knowing that our program was determined largely by financial considerations. The rest of the program was conducted as part of the continuing-health and therapy plan, or Phase Three, and was operated on a fee-for-service basis. We were able to keep the fee for this continuing therapy quite low because of the important roles played by the community and alumni volunteers.

As was usually the case with our new clinics, we ran into a few problems with the Donwood operation following its opening. I had expected that we might have a year to hit our full capacity. This would have given us time to find and train staff to meet the patient load that would increase from nine, as at the Bell Clinic, to forty-nine. The only experienced staff we had in the early days were our Bell Clinic personnel.

While planning the construction of Donwood, I had no illusions about the difficulty of finding qualified clinical staff to work in the addiction field. Accordingly, I worked with the architects to include wiring for audio instruction in all the bedrooms, and audio-visual equipment in the common-rooms on three floors. A master control room could transmit five separate instruction programs simultaneously to any bedroom and three audio-visual programs to the lounges. Various experts worked together to produce a headset with optimal sound and comfort. Each night the patients received repeated instruction in progressive relaxation as an alternative to the use of sedatives. For this purpose, Mary Epp's voice was immortalized for hundreds of patients. Eventually, as additional competent staff were retained, it became a less important part of the recovery program. Since I had put the nine-part chart on videotape and we also regularly used some of my earlier films, initially the nurses had additional jobs as projectionists and discussion leaders.

When we realized that we were operating at full patient capacity within the first three months, we had to scramble to hire sufficient new staff, and again I had to rely on nurses to provide the stability and flexibility we needed during that transition period. We were successful in integrating new nurses into responsible roles in the program, including the management of the audio-visual control room. The training was continuous and on the job, with veteran Bell Clinic staff providing the instruction. In the meantime, we had much more trouble finding new physicians willing to work full- or part-time, since not many were yet prepared to risk professional careers by associating themselves with the treatment of alcoholics. It was apparent that by 1967 the medical profession as a whole was still reluctant to become involved in the treatment of alcoholism and other addictions.

Initially I also had some difficulty explaining to the Ministry of Health why meals at Donwood would cost more than they did at other hospitals. I wanted mealtimes to become a significant component of the whole therapy process. We learned way back at Glenmaple that tasty, nutritious food was an important part of a general plan to provide a pleasant environment for our patients. (Alcoholics were notorious for checking out prematurely from many treatment facilities.) Our idea was to keep the patients involved in the recovery process long enough for them to become motivated to participate in the total therapy program. We also wanted to promote their long-term interest in new eating patterns that stressed sound nutrition. The nutritionist, kitchen, and dining-room staff, therefore, became vital members of our treatment team.

Of course the patients required more than just good food and primary care. We needed able people to help organize and provide ongoing support in the continuing-therapy part of our treatment. At the Bell Clinic all staff members had worked in all three phases of recovery. Now we had to discover and develop a new class of personnel to support the continuing-health and therapy program. The nurses had their hands full just managing the detoxification unit, daily patient care, and assisting with the education component of the treatment plan. At that stage we were able to hire psychologists and other qualified therapists, and under their direction we introduced routine group psychotherapy to all our patients.

There were still many people who believed that only an alcoholic could help another alcoholic. I disagreed, and made certain that I would not turn over the entire responsibility for continuing-care and counseling to the patients themselves, as I had done at Shadow Brook, until they had been at least one year into their recovery. This did not mean that I distrusted the ability of AA to help my new patients. Our patients were urged to attend regular AA meetings and I arranged with the fellowship to establish a "Donwood Group" (which still meets weekly). I knew that just as AA could provide a supportive community, so could non-addicted people be part of a supportive network. I believed that there were many people in the Leaside area who could fill this friendly supportive role, who might have sufficient time on their hands and be willing to help. There was some irony in the fact that I was about to seek such people in the very community that had initially been so alarmed at the prospect of having a treatment center for alcoholics so close to their homes.

One of the members of our board of directors found a woman who was interested in volunteering to work with our patients. She followed a four-week training session, and experienced the same month-long treatment and counseling program that the patients themselves did. She learned firsthand about addiction and problems in recovery and how to function with the backup of the clinical staff. The plan worked out very well, and she soon told her friends and neighbors about it. Before long we had a group of mature and concerned neighborhood women working with us, and they were welcomed by the patients. These volunteers told their families and friends about their work, and soon many of the people in the Leaside area knew more about what was happening in the Donwood Institute than in any of the other rehabilitation centers bordering their community. I devoted considerable thought to a suitable name for these volunteers, and finally decided that they should be called "clinical secretaries." Their genuine concern, understanding, and compassion became a very significant part of our entire recovery program. I considered our development of these positions and the subsequent use of the alumni to have been two of the most significant demonstrations of community involvement in our work.

Toward the end of the first year, things were settling down at Donwood. Not only were we developing a reliable team of staff and volunteers, but we had been able to recruit three very capable physicians with backgrounds in general practice. They joined the staff on a full-time basis and provided a predictable, stable, and competent medical base for our operation. One of them had also recovered from alcohol addiction himself through the Donwood program. In 1967, as well as opening Donwood, I was awarded the Centennial Medal "in recognition of valuable service to the nation." This was the first official recognition of my work in Canada.

By 1969, our staff had stabilized and we had a fairly lengthy waiting list of patients. I felt that it was time to review our success rate, and a research project entitled "An Evaluation of The Donwood Institute Treatment Plan" was undertaken with funds generously provided by the William and Martha Ford Fund and the American Association Against Addiction. The study was carried out by Toby Levinson, a psychologist who was working part-time for us. The first report of the study was published in the *Ontario Medical Review* in May 1971. It was repeated on the same patients at three years and five years post-treatment, and we were encouraged by the result, which indicated that over sixty percent of them had benefitted from our treatment.

Later in 1969 Harvey Firestone suggested that Donwood should apply to be recognized as a public charity by the U.S. Treasury Department. Our lawyer, Jack Miller, was astounded at the suggestion, and thought it impossible. Nonetheless, Harvey Firestone arranged for a Cleveland lawyer who had formerly worked at the U.S. Treasury Department to explore the idea and in a surprisingly short time our Canadian Donwood was recognized as a public charity in the United States! When Jack Miller heard the news, he was sufficiently moved to comment, "It's enough to restore one's faith in bureaucracy."

Two other significant events occurred in 1969 to further re-establish my involvement in the United States. I became a special lecturer at the Rutgers Summer School of Alcohol Studies in New Brunswick, New Jersey, a position I retained until 1975, when I decided to cut back on my outside activities to protect my health. At about the same time that I joined the staff at Rutgers, Harvey Firestone began to insist that I write a book, so at age fifty-nine I arranged to take some time off to concentrate on the project. *Escape from Addiction* was published by McGraw-Hill in New York in 1970. The book represented my philosophy and ideas at that time on the problems and treatment of addiction, and it was distributed in the United States and Canada.

Linda, our middle child, had been born into a home which as a matter of course accepted alcoholics as patients, who on more than one occasion had rocked her to sleep. She first worked for me during her high-school years when she was employed at the Bell Clinic for three summers and she demonstrated a natural aptitude in assisting in a variety of clinical and administrative situations. She elected to pursue a career in the business world and began by working as a secretary in various business offices. In 1971 she was working in Kingston, Ontario, as a legal secretary. I persuaded her that she could have a role to play at Donwood, and invited her to explore the rewards and hazards of working with us. Also, her love of skydiving had inspired in me a natural fatherly desire to offer her alternative and perhaps less dangerous challenges.

Linda joined the staff in March, on the understanding that she would accompany me on out-of-town engagements and assist in developing new programs. Her first special task at Donwood was to help develop a program for the families of our patients, to introduce family members to much of the same orientation that the patients followed. Originally it was a course held on Saturday mornings to help families understand the objectives of the recovery process and to encourage them to become supportively involved.

We recorded all the sessions and over the next few months edited the tapes to develop a written lecture series. This included transcripts of the questions and answers from the audience. The next step was to organize a three-and-a-half-day education and therapy program for families, to be offered monthly. Family members who could not attend because of distance were sent a copy of the written lecture series each week. It was much like a correspondence course. It took a year before we had earned the full support of the rest of the staff for this new concept. After this it was regarded as an integral part of our addiction-recovery plan. The results were gratifying, and thereafter the family program ran every second week. An extensive recruiting exercise was developed to encourage family members to attend the short course and then join the continuing-therapy sessions with the patients.

All patients were accepted for treatment on the understanding that they would agree to participate in the three-phase treatment program for a minimum of two years. In the first phase, the medical staff treated any acute condition such as intoxication or withdrawal and the management of other medical problems, then conducted a careful examination of the patients' physical, mental, and social status. This information formed the basis for his or her participation in the various components of the treatment program.

In the second phase, the multi-disciplinary staff included physicians, nurses, psychologists, social workers, dieticians, technicians, physiotherapists, physical-education and relaxation instructors, a chaplain, and individuals who had recovered from their addictions. This staff assumed the responsibility for the first four weeks of therapy, education, and counseling, much of which was done on a group basis. As a result, patients could begin to see and feel the benefits from their steady improvement in health. They began to realize that they had no alternative but to learn how to live in another way. In short, the orientation program aimed to provide the insights that are so well expressed in the well-known prayer adopted by AA, "God grant me the serenity to accept the things I cannot change, the courage to change the things I can, and the wisdom to know the difference."

The long-term goals of the health and recovery program at Donwood — and today at Bellwood — were and still are: the interruption and progressive inactivation of dependence on alcohol and drugs, optimal repair of the related problems, and involvement in a total-health program directed toward a balanced improvement in physical, psychological, social and spiritual well-being.

The third phase now involves one or more meetings a week to sustain and reinforce these goals during the first year, and bi-monthly meetings in the second. Therein lies the most significant feature of the plan — it never really ends. In fact we consider it the introduction to a continual growth experience. The concept was borrowed in part from AA. However, it differs in two areas — in the initial steps we take to lead the addict to a new life, and in the fact that it has been designed to integrate its participants more effectively into the outside community. The changes we made along the way resulted from the lessons we learned from all our patients, and the responses we developed to meet their needs.

In the continuing-therapy program, the first director, George Birtch, was responsible for maintaining unbroken contact with patients for a minimum period of two years. For the first part of the patient's recovery program, he was assisted by the clinical secretaries, who knew the recovery plan for each patient and maintained weekly contact with that person during the first year. These women usually operated on their own time, and integrated their clinical work into their family lives and other activities as their schedules permitted. Their role was to befriend and encourage patients and families in good times and bad, host the weekly meetings, and send a personal note to patients along with our regular weekly letter. They all took their responsibilities very seriously and were remarkably effective working with the patients.

Most of the primary and secondary damage from addiction will clear up with abstinence over a long enough period, along with continuous attention to good nutrition and a general good-health program. But if a patient continued to have serious problems, the clinical secretary either referred his or her case to an appropriate member of the professional staff, or obtained instruction on how she could handle the situation herself. If a patient relapsed, she'd tell him or her to stop drinking and get to a Donwood or an AA meeting. An amazing percentage did just that.

The alumni also assisted in several ways during the first year. At Donwood a recovered patient was hired as a full-time assistant to the director of the continuing-therapy program. Veterans of the Donwood plan who passed through the special hazards of that first year and were willing and able to accept responsibility for another patient's health, acted as special assistants to the clinical secretaries and assumed most of the responsibilities for the follow-up meetings during the latter part of the patient's first year. The alumni developed their own association and initiated a variety of social, educational, and recreational activities for patients and their families. Patients were strongly advised to attend AA meetings, and we maintained contact with those from out of town by weekly correspondence or by telephone. The follow-up health and recovery therapy was designed as an essential extension of the "caring-community" support system.

When George Birtch's status as a clergyman became more appreciated by both patients and staff, he was asked to officiate at weddings and baptisms, and to be a counselor for spiritual problems. Although George subsequently left to become pastor of Fairlawn United Church in Toronto, he retained his association with Donwood. When his term at the church ended, he worked with us again in our efforts to add a spiritual dimension to our total health effort. Thanks in large part to AA, we learned that those who found new purpose in life had the best chance of recovering from addiction. The way for them to discover this new purpose was to explore their unique resources and to use them positively to help themselves and others.

Although stricken by cancer, George accepted the challenge with his customary vigor, and the programs he developed over the years are now a standard part of our treatment plans. His work at Donwood, which became a positive factor in a new rewarding life for both patients and other staff, continued and expanded as we developed the new program at Bellwood Health Services. His impact on hardened cocaine addicts and others, who had never considered a spiritual dimension to their lives, was a powerful component of the total program. He persisted in carrying on as spiritual counselor until his cancer was so advanced that he could no longer walk up the steps into our building. His death in October 1988 was mourned by thousands of patients and their families, as well as countless others who had known the unique rewards of having him as a lifetime friend.

We were quite pleased when in 1971 we were able to lease additional space from the nearby Northlea United Church for our program work. We needed the extra space primarily to accommodate our new family program, since we had already outgrown the Donwood facilities. Many of the people who had been so alarmed at the prospect of an addiction-treatment center in their neighborhood were members of the Northlea Church, and so were many of Donwood's clinical secretaries.

The Northlea arrangement was supposed to be temporary, but it continues to this day. Indeed, the uses of the church have been expanded to encompass a wide variety of Donwood activities, including a program for the teenage children of our patients. It was gratifying for me to be able to integrate addiction-related programs into the activities of a busy regional church, for it is ideally suited to house a caring-community program that requires large meeting rooms and no stigmas.

In 1973 we were continuing to operate with a waiting list of several hundred names. I approached the Ministry of Health for its support in developing a controlled study to assess the possibility that many of our patients would do equally well if treated on an out-patient basis. The ministry agreed, and my colleagues and I evaluated one hundred applicants as potentially suitable for such a program. We based our judgment on criteria any hospital would apply when determining whether or not a patient was suitable for in-patient or out-patient care — the patient's primary diagnosis of alcoholism, whether or not the patient required a hospital bed for detoxification and/or for management of physical health problems, and whether or not the patient could commute to Donwood. Once we had selected the suitable candidates from the general population applying for treatment, they were randomly divided into two groups of equal size and assigned to either the day-clinic operation or the in-patient service. The treatment, instruction, and counseling programs were comparable for the two groups. Since there was no space for an out-patient program at Donwood or Northlea Church, we arranged for the use of the nearby MacLean House, which was located on property owned by Sunnybrook Medical Centre. The house was a magnificent mansion with beautiful grounds, and had been the former residence of J. S. MacLean, a successful Toronto businessman. We had it remodeled, refurnished, and prepared for the day-clinic operations.

The results of our study strongly indicated that carefully selected patients could be treated on an out-patient basis with results comparable to those obtained with in-patients. Consequently, we proceeded with our plans for a fully operational day clinic.

In 1974 psychologist Toby Levinson completed her five-year study of treatment results at the Donwood Institute. She had been able to contact and assess ninety percent of the original group of 154 patients she had studied in 1969. After five years, forty-one percent were rated as recovered or significantly improved, twenty-one percent were moderately improved, and thirty-eight percent were unchanged or had deteriorated. The study clearly supported our belief in the importance of continuing our health and support service for at least two years, and led to our eventual decision at Bellwood to continue a follow-up support program for five years.

The Canadian Council on Hospital Accreditation contacted us in 1976 to ask if we might help to develop guidelines for the accreditation of addiction treatment programs. Since we were neither a general nor a psychiatric hospital, it was decided that we should be examined according to the criteria for both. Wonderful, I thought; what had I gotten us into this time! This required a great deal of work, much of which was done by our then medical director, Dr. Douglas Macdonald, and the head nurse, Rosemary McNaughton. (Mary Epp had retired a year earlier.) It was through their efforts that Donwood became the first addiction treatment hospital in Canada to be accredited by the council. This official recognition set an important precedent and marked a particularly encouraging turning point in the perception of addiction treatment in this country. Two years later we prepared for our second examination for accreditation, and were pleased when we received a three-year approval, the longest that the council granted and our program continued to operate smoothly as we modified and improved its various components.

For the first time since 1965, I was frustrated to discover that I had to slow down again and pay some attention to my own health. In the fall of 1977 I began to notice occasional pains in my chest and realized that it was probably angina. When I saw my friend Bill Hall about it, he reminded me I was sixty-six years old, not thirty-nine, and he immediately sent me to the Toronto Rehabilitation Centre, then under the direction of Dr. Terrence Kavanagh. I was enrolled in the progressive controlled-exercise program for which the institution is famous. For over two years, five days a week, I followed the exercise prescriptions of the center in all seasons, in all weather, wherever I might be.

Regardless of anything else I was doing, the exercises became a regular part of my life even when I was away from home attending conferences. I increased my distance from one mile in twenty minutes to four miles in fifty-nine minutes and gradually lost all fear of my early warm-up chest pains with each walking episode, as the pain periods shortened over the months. The angina finally disappeared altogether while I was in Barbados with Mary on a short winter vacation, about eighteen months after I had begun the regimen. I continued the program faithfully for many months after this, and finally began to replace the organized exercise program with a more informal pattern of walking at whatever pace I felt comfortable, and with gardening.

In 1979 over 500 people were on our waiting list and we felt the need to design a better system to respond more quickly to people that we could not admit when they needed us. Tragically, some of them either committed suicide or died from complications of addiction before we could treat them. We set up a task force to review our medical services and our intake and assessment procedures again. Our plan was to develop an orientation program for people on the waiting list, and to design a family-oriented early intervention program that would operate in the evenings. Individuals who came to us in the early stages of alcohol or drug dependence could then be treated on an evening out-patient basis without losing any time from work and without occupying a hospital bed.

The planning was completed by the end of the year, and by February 1980 we were training staff, alumni, and community volunteers to help implement the new services. Again, we needed more space to operate and we purchased portable buildings, which we located on the adjacent Divadale property that we had finally purchased from the University of Toronto in 1978. We used the smaller buildings as offices and classrooms, but they were quite chilly in the winter and hot in the summer. Staff members now ran back and forth between the main Donwood building and Northlea Church, two blocks away, between MacLean House a mile and a half away and the portables next door. The elaborate telephone system installed to accommodate the needs of our sprawling operation was most impressive.

In order to determine which patients on the waiting list

were candidates for our new evening program, we established a pre-admission assessment initially done by the physicians and later by the nurses. We also devised an orientation and support program on Tuesday and Thursday evenings from 6:00 to 7:30 P.M. for local prospective patients and their families who were on the waiting list for in-patient or day-clinic programs. This six-week program was operated by nurses and alumni volunteers, and became the first step in the treatment program. Seventy-five to ninety patients and their families attended the weekly sessions.

We launched our evening out-patient service in May 1980. Unfortunately, unlike the development of our day clinic years earlier, we received no funding from the Ministry of Health for this pilot project. We had to hire new staff, who worked with our alumni and community volunteers, and we were forced to charge patients for the service. Many of them considered our $1,500 fee for the two-year program excessive, even though it covered only a fraction of the cost of one year's supply of alcohol or drugs for most of the applicants. As a result, the evening program did not operate at capacity, and I was uncomfortably reminded of the early days when our financial position was often precarious.

In 1981, we were forced to make cuts in our family-service department, and the research department had to be discontinued entirely. Even so, our financial situation continued to deteriorate. Some members of our board felt that my insistence in developing the evening service was impractical, and that continuing it would only increase the drain on our finances. But I wanted to continue the program, and I decided to set out to raise new funds somehow. The fact that interest rates were then running around twenty percent did not make life any easier, and it required two more years of effort before we were successful. I see now that the only problem with the evening out-patient plan was that it was ahead of its time. The Ministry of Health is now encouraging and supporting more and more out-patient programs, because they are less expensive than in-patient care.

Because of this and other problems, I was becoming increasingly frustrated at Donwood. We needed new treatment programs to handle a whole new set of addiction problems, particularly in younger people, but we could not get government backing to analyze and develop them. Probably for financial reasons government agencies throughout Canada were shying away from funding new projects in the addiction field, at a time when they were desperately needed. At the same time we began to realize that our treatment programs for alcohol addiction would also have to be updated to deal with rapid changes in patterns of chemical abuse. Many of our Donwood patients were addicted not only to alcohol, but to other chemical substances at the same time, and we needed new programs to deal with these cross addictions.

"Carol" was a typical example of this phenomenon. Carol's primary addiction was to benzodiazepine. When she was admitted to Donwood she said she was taking from five to ten mg. of Valium per day. We suspected that the dosage was higher. Her secondary addiction was to alcohol. She drank vodka and red wine to increase the effect of the tranquilizer, which she needed every morning to get going. She had used Valium for three years, and had probably been dependent on it for two. The amount she took increased dramatically during the six-month period before her admission to Donwood. But her tolerance for the drug also rose during that time, and she drank secretly to increase its effect. She began suffering from blackouts, anxiety, and other unpleasant side-effects. On one occasion she accidentally overdosed with Valium and alcohol.

Carol was fairly typical of the type of person we were beginning to see more frequently at Donwood. She was in her twenties, rebellious, and had experimented in her teens with various types of street drugs. She suffered from migraine headaches, for which she was prescribed Valium and a strong analgesic with codeine. She did not have an ideal marriage and was not very interested in her office job. Eventually she increased her use of Valium to escape her unhappiness. At the same time she began drinking more, which resulted in a release of pent-up anger she was unable to vent when sober. She came to Donwood soon after her employer fired her, because her addiction problems had adversely affected her performance. Her husband also wanted her to seek help for her dependence.

Carol did not see alcohol as a problem, but she reluctantly agreed to take Temposil for several months, although she felt pressured by her husband to do so. She had a short, one-time relapse with alcohol two months after leaving Donwood. However, she got back into her recovery program after she and her husband re-established contact with her recovery counselor following her relapse. Fortunately, she was able to overcome her dependence on Valium.

Although Carol and her husband did not become enthusiastically involved in Donwood's Phase Three, or in AA or Narcotics Anonymous, their relationship improved, and she found enjoyable employment. But other patients with similar backgrounds were not doing so well, and we did not yet know enough about the newer "in" drugs to deal with them effectively. When cocaine first became popular, many experts did not consider it to be addictive. Moreover, many people with cross addictions could not even be admitted to Donwood when they most needed help, because we did not have room for them.

I was becoming convinced that the bureaucratic obstacles we faced in trying to explore new programs in a public hospital, like Donwood, were almost overwhelming. I would have trouble making a significant contribution to Donwood's operations and expansion of services. I felt compelled to explore new approaches to programs to meet the challenges of the 1980s, and I even began to think of severing my ties with the clinical operations at Donwood. For the Bell family, it was another case of déjà vu.

CHAPTER THIRTEEN

Travel and Recognition

Although I continued to have difficulty gaining support for an expansion of our services in Canada, interest in our work in the United States steadily increased throughout the Donwood period. Partly because of my involvement with Harvey Firestone and William Clay Ford, I again became actively involved in the U.S. And I was free to travel more, as the Donwood operation had developed an excellent staff.

In 1972 Harvey Firestone and the American Association Against Addiction (AAAA), together with the National Council on Alcoholism in New York City, arranged for me to present a series of seminars in five major industrial cities in the United States — Detroit, St. Louis, Pittsburgh, Houston, and Los Angeles. My daughter Linda accompanied me on these occasions as my general assistant. Mr. Firestone's personal influence with the heads of major corporations meant that these seminars were well attended by representatives of the important industries in each city. One incidental function of these seminars was the promotion of my book, *Escape From Addiction,* the publication of which had been sponsored by the AAAA. These appearances also enabled me to re-establish contact with some of the medical directors with whom I had been associated about twenty years earlier when I was chairman of the Committee on Problem Drinking of the Industrial Medical Association.

The most memorable seminar on this tour was in Los Angeles, the last city we visited. After my presentation there I was approached by a naval officer, Captain Joseph Zuska, who told me that the U.S. Navy had set up a treatment center at Long Beach, California, for personnel who had developed problems with alcohol. They were using some of my earlier films in their program. He invited me to come down to Long Beach to address his staff and patients. I agreed, and much to our delight Linda and I were chauffeured to the naval base in a Rolls-Royce. I addressed the group, which included all ranks from ordinary seamen to an admiral, and thoroughly enjoyed the opportunity to meet and talk with this very active, vigorous-looking group. As we left, Captain Zuska promised to keep in touch with us.

It wasn't long before I heard from the U.S. Navy again. In April 1972 I received a call from Captain James Baxter. By that time the navy had accepted the fact that it had an alcoholism problem among some of its personnel, and had decided to establish treatment centers in fifteen navy hospitals around the world. Captain Baxter's responsibility was to find suitable training services for the key personnel who would staff these special treatment units, so he had talked with Captain Zuska, who was in charge of the pilot treatment center at Long Beach.

The captain told us he wished to arrange for The Donwood Institute to provide the training services, and he wanted the first group of trainees to start their training two months later, in June. The trainees would consist of fifteen naval physicians and fifteen men from other ranks, many of whom had themselves recovered from alcoholism through the Fellowship of Alcoholics Anonymous. We agreed to organize the program and expected the "students" as scheduled.

Many of the physicians were psychiatrists, and along with the other personnel selected for initial training they were astounded to receive an abrupt order to attend a special training course — in Toronto. Most of the men, if not all, had never heard of Donwood, and were more than a little annoyed to receive an order to report to a small hospital in another country. The officers were also irritated at having to associate with those of lower rank, and those of lower rank seemed equally unhappy at having to associate with the officers. One officer from the Guantanamo Bay Naval Base on the southeast shore of Cuba was particularly angry. He had been told only to report to a certain address in Toronto on a particular date. When he found out he was expected to be trained in the treatment of alcoholics, he was even more enraged. The final straw for him was to discover that his partner for the duration of the program was a noncommissioned officer he had never met.

I selected three of our most experienced group therapists and told them that I had a special role for them — to get the trainees to work together. We divided the men into three groups of ten, half officers and half other ranks, and hoped that our therapists were equal to the task of coping with the expected emotional storms. I figured that after several years' experience in dealing with many ornery alcoholics, our therapists were tough and smart enough to manage the situation. They were, although it wasn't easy. The naval psychiatrists in particular were not pleased at being the subjects in group psychotherapy sessions led by psychologists.

The trainees were not hesitant about expressing their feelings toward one another and their doubts about the validity of the program. But once this common ground had been established and their reservations stated, they seemed to accept the program and each other better, particularly those in the lower ranks. Before the course was finished, men of all ranks were much friendlier with one another and co-operating together. I was especially pleased (and somewhat amused) to see the officer from Guantanamo Bay and his NCO partner frequently taking walks together in the off-work hours.

Captain Baxter and his associates must have been pleased with the results too, because we were asked to accept another forty trainees in the fall of 1972. Although this was a larger group, we had less difficulty with them because the navy had briefed them more thoroughly about the type of training they would receive, and there was less conflict between the different ranks than there had been on the first occasion. After his course, one graduate from the naval base in Oakland, California, wrote back to say that the first person he had encountered on sick parade when he returned to his base was a man suffering from the shakes, sweats, and general hyperactivity associated with alcohol withdrawal. He said that for the first time in his navy career he had sat down and talked with the man, who was so amazed and overcome by his concern that he had broken down and wept.

Although we had been advised that there would be additional personnel coming for the training, this did not happen. I never learned the whole story, but I understand that a senior officer became very annoyed when he learned that the U.S. Navy was sending its personnel out of the country for training. However, as Baxter put it, "At least it worked long enough to get us headed in the right direction." So my association with the navy officially ended almost twenty years after I had first learned of their problems with alcoholic personnel. When I had been chairman of the Committee on Problem Drinking, medical personnel often attended our conventions and, on more than one occasion, came to me to discuss the problem of drinking in the navy. They felt totally helpless to do anything about it, because such an admission would have threatened their macho image and one of the navy's longstanding traditions — that its men could hold their liquor.

In an ironic way we also became involved in training personnel from the Canadian Armed Forces during the same period. In 1972 we were told that the military had first contacted Washington for advice about where they could send personnel for training. Washington referred them back to us at the Donwood. So in 1973 our training services for the Department of National Defence (DND) got underway.

The first to arrive were the chaplains. They came five at a time, stayed for one month, and became acquainted with all phases of the Donwood program. They were followed a year later by DND physicians, who attended our courses along with health-care professionals referred to us by the American Association Against Addiction. Courses were run three times a year for several years. In 1974 we actually put on a total of five courses for various groups, and our staff were rapidly becoming accustomed to their dual roles as therapists and teachers. And our military students were quite impressed by the Donwood alumni we often selected to participate in the courses.

The DND went on to establish six alcoholism treatment centers based on the Donwood plan, one in West Germany and five across Canada. The department has done one-year follow-up studies from 1977 to 1987 inclusive on the 5,619 patients who passed through the program during that decade. The success rate after the one-year period has been seventy-six percent, perhaps the best evidence we have to date that the treatment program we developed over the years can be quite successful.

This period was not without its sad moments. On June 1, 1973, Harvey Firestone died of cancer. He was the person most responsible for my renewed activities and recognition in the United States. Although small in stature, he was impressive in many other ways. He applied his courage, wisdom, and administrative skills to expand the understanding and management of alcohol-related problems in his country, particularly in the business community. He accomplished this through his funding and support of the various activities of the AAAA. He was a warm, delightful man who had given my family and me many happy memories. His death was a great loss to all who had known and worked with him.

After Harvey Firestone's death, I again had the opportunity of traveling to Africa. In 1974 the director of the International Council on Alcohol and Addiction invited me to be a keynote speaker at the first South African International Conference on Alcoholism and Drug Dependence, in Cape Town. I suggested to Mary that she should come along, and she readily agreed. I also convinced my longtime friend, Grant Brown, and his wife, Dorothy, to join us. The Bells and the Browns had an unforgettable five-week holiday on the African continent, the highlight of which was a visit to the Serengeti Plain and the Ngora-Ngora Crater as part of a safari tour in Kenya and Tanzania.

The Ngora-Ngora Crater is about ten miles in diameter and a mile below the circular rim; this plain is home to every variety of wildlife in the region. Descending to the floor of the crater, we rode in four-wheel-drive Land-Rovers that negotiated dangerously narrow hairpin turns on the rough roads. On the way back up, I was sitting on the side of the Land-Rover nearest to the crater and I had a beautiful view of the rocky hillside clear to the bottom. I nudged Grant sitting beside me, pointed over the side, and began to sing softly, "Nearer My God to Thee." Grant peered over and immediately joined in. We did not realize that our driver was quite proficient in English, and also a Christian convert. He began to laugh so hard that we were worried he really would lose control of the Land-Rover and take us all to meet our Maker. Before we flew on to Johannesburg, Mary and I took a side trip to the Olduvai Gorge where, in the 1960s, Louis and Mary Leakey had discovered pre-human skeletal remains over one million years old. I had always enjoyed reading about anthropology, so this was a wonderful experience.

My talk in Capetown consisted of a general overview of the clinical management of addiction disorders. One of the people at the conference was Japie Starker, a psychologist in charge of an alcoholism treatment center in Pretoria. Japie, who had overcome paraplegia as a result of childhood poliomyelitis, approached me after my talk with many questions about the Donwood Institute, its programs, philosophy, staffing, and so on. He asked if it would be possible for us to accept him for a month or so of special training. He was very pleased to hear that we had already been training groups from the United States and Canada and assured me that he would be in touch. The following year he came to Donwood and stayed for five weeks. He quickly became very popular with our staff, and his stay was a happy and rewarding experience for all of us. I heard from him again six years later. He informed me that a study done in South Africa comparing the results of treatment in twenty different addiction treatment centers there had concluded that his clinic, which had been modeled on the Donwood plan, was the most effective.

In 1979 I was surprised to receive two awards. The first was presented in June 1979, when I was appointed a life member of the Ontario Medical Association at its annual meeting. One of the physicians at the reception prior to the awards was Dr. Kirk Lyon, who had been president of the OMA and chairman of the committee that had investigated our operation at Shadow Brook thirty years before. We had been suspected of some kind of malpractice or medical racketeering. In the ensuing years I had come to know this fine physician, and he had referred several patients to us for treatment. The same was true for Dr. Victor Johnson, the founder of the Canadian College of General Practice, also a member of that original inspection committee. When I entered the reception room and saw Dr. Lyon, he looked up at me with a twinkle in his eye and said, "Well, this is quite a switch, isn't it?"

The greatest thrill came in December, when I learned

that I had been appointed an officer of the Order of Canada, and was to be formally inducted in April 1980. There are three levels of the Order, the most prestigious being "Companion," the next "Officer," and the third "Member." Twice annually about sixty Canadians are appointed to the Order, which Queen Elizabeth II established in 1967 to recognize outstanding achievement and service in various fields of human endeavor. The chancellor and principal companion of the Order is the governor general of Canada, who was at that time His Excellency the Right Honourable Edward Schreyer. It was indeed a very special moment when I stood in Rideau Hall before the governor general and the audience, consisting of all the other recipients, their families, Chief Justice, the Honourable Bora Laskin, and other members of the advisory council. In my turn I stood and listened to a brief citation of my work, and when I stepped forward for the governor general to put the medal around my neck I could hardly believe that it was happening.

Much to my surprise I received two more honors in 1980. Two months after receiving the Order of Canada, I was appointed a senior member of the Canadian Medical Association. A month later, the International Assembly of Alcoholics Anonymous invited me to address their conference at the Superdome in New Orleans. This was the forty-fifth anniversary of the founding of AA, and the International Assembly, which is held every five years, brought together thousands of members from all parts of the world.

For me the trip to New Orleans was a fitting climax to a period of my life when I was finally able to reflect on the tremendous advances in treating addiction that had been achieved over the years. We owed that progress in no small part to the lessons we had learned from our patients, who continued to intrigue us with their ingenuity, honesty, and desire to lead fruitful, sober lives. But those attending the meeting also reminded me of the constant challenges we faced in responding to the needs of people struggling with addiction problems. And the fact that so many countries were represented at this international gathering was an affirmation of the pandemic nature of alcoholism and other forms of chemical dependency. It was a distinct honor for me to speak to this international group of recovered alcoholics, and to compliment them on the roles their peers had played in the development of the programs we used to treat them. My unwavering conviction that total abstinence is the only way to recovery from addiction had originated from my experiences back in 1946 with my first patients and my introduction to the AA movement.

CHAPTER FOURTEEN

From Donwood to Bellwood

During the 1970s public attention in North America and around the world was increasingly drawn to the widespread problems of alcohol and drug addiction. This was accompanied by a rapid acceleration of interest in establishing effective programs of treatment and prevention. One development in the United States was the formation of the National Institute of Alcohol Abuse and Alcoholism in Washington, D.C., which was provided with substantial funds for research and education. The industrial community continued to take the lead in effective intervention and management of alcohol and drug abuse, and many companies throughout the United States and Canada set up employee-assistance programs to help their personnel with addiction problems.

One of the major breakthroughs was developed by the Johnson Institute in Minneapolis, Minnesota. A basic premise for effective involvement in the AA program had been that the alcoholics themselves had to ask for help. This meant that, first, many of them had to lose everything, hit rock bottom, before they could begin the long road to recovery. The Johnson Institute pioneered the development of an effective technique in the early intervention of alcohol and drug addiction, by training concerned family members, friends, and/or occupational associates to jointly confront a resistive addict.

By bringing close family members and concerned other people together, and training them to present a united caring front to counter all efforts at manipulation by the addict, the victims of addiction can be directed toward effective help long before totally destroying themselves. This, and other new techniques, coupled with a rapid increase in awareness that effective treatment programs can successfully combat addiction, led to the establishment of hundreds of new treatment centers all over the United States. Unfortunately, such was not the case in Canada.

The core element in the vast majority of these new treatment services was an intensive introduction to and involvement in the Fellowship of Alcoholics Anonymous. Family members of the addict were introduced to offshoot organizations — Al-Anon for spouses, and Alateen for children of alcoholics. Depending on the clinic, the involvement of physicians and other health-care professionals in dealing with related clinical and social problems varied greatly from nil to full integration with the basic AA program.

In addition to these new organizations, many private general hospitals in the U.S. with the space available set up their own treatment units. They also advertised these services to the public. Public figures in both government and entertainment circles, who were quite open about their own recovery from alcoholism or drug addiction, became role models for many others. For a while it seemed as if some well-known American personality was checking into the Betty Ford Clinic in Palm Springs, California, just about every week. In the United States there was a rapid change in public attitude, as the wraps were removed from a formerly shameful and unmentionable condition.

There was a corresponding increase in the desire for treatment of alcoholism in Canada, but it was not accompanied by any real increase in access to treatment services. Many industries in Canada with employee-assistance programs soon gave up trying to get their patients into Donwood with its three-month waiting list, and looked for adequate treatment south of the border. We at Donwood were frustrated by our inability to convince government agencies of our need to expand, and further dismayed that government health services in Canada automatically paid seventy-five percent of the cost for treatment in accredited private U.S. institutions.

I took a close look at what was happening in the United States, where this expansion often included the development of many corporate-chain operations. I decided to explore the possibility of selling similar rights to market the Donwood program to another major health-care provider within Canada. We took the concept to our accountants, who referred us in turn to a consulting firm that specialized in franchising. This lead to discussions with Extendicare, a private, profit-oriented health-care company that specializes in the operation of medical laboratories and nursing homes. Besides offering greater access to treatment, a franchise arrangement, we felt, would produce long-term revenues to support our own research and evaluation studies.

A corporate identity was necessary for this new concept, so the idea of Donwood Health Services Inc. was born. The company would have the right to market any or all of the Donwood services through a contractual arrangement between the Donwood Institute and the company. The reason for the separate entity was that we wanted to ensure that the Donwood Institute global budget from the Ministry of Health was not jeopardized by an infusion of funds from another source.

Extendicare dropped their interest in the project in the fall of 1982, when the Ministry of Health refused to officially approve the new plan. When that happened I turned to my daughter, Linda, and said, "Let's proceed with a new plan of our own." She agreed enthusiastically. She had spent the better part of the past year working on the project, and the Bell family had already contributed over

$22,000 to bring the plan that far. We gave up the franchising idea altogether. I was happy with the decision, because I had been concerned about our ability to maintain quality control under such an arrangement.

This time we turned to the Associated Senior Executives of Canada Limited (a group of businessmen who apparently did not know what the word retirement meant) and requested their assistance in developing a business and marketing plan. These executives had a wealth of experience in all areas of business, and over the next two years they became actively involved in developing a five-year plan for us. They worked directly with Linda, and I stayed out of their way for the most part to concentrate on exploring the routes open to us to finance the proposed new operation and to receive government support and approval.

My responsibility for finding additional operating revenue for Donwood ceased in February 1983, when the Ministry of Health finally approved funding for our evening health-treatment service. With this welcome development I felt there was no more I could do at Donwood, and I began plans to withdraw from it altogether. Linda and I changed the name of the new corporation to Bellwood Health Services Inc., an independent operation. Its name was based on the two treatment centers that had preceded it, the Bell Clinic and the Donwood Institute, as well as the old family farm where I was born and raised, which had also been named Bellwood. We deliberately chose the term "health services" rather than "hospital," "clinic," "foundation," or "institute," because we wanted to emphasize our primary concern with total health, and not just addiction.

In May I received a phone call from my son, Ron, who lived in Regina. He had become a father a couple of days earlier, and was now reporting that their newborn son had Down's Syndrome. Since his wife, Eleanor, was on maternity leave and Ron was free for the summer, I suggested that they spend some time with us in Toronto. Ron could help me work on finalizing plans for the new company, and we would all be close together during that difficult time.

Accordingly, Ron, who has a Ph.D. in psychology, designed a research project for our purposes with Dr. Grant Macdonald, a professor of social work at Toronto's York University. The project surveyed the number of Canadians going to the United States for addiction treatment, and the subsequent costs incurred by the various provincial governments. We contacted the Ontario Ministry of Health, but they could not help us, since their computers could not provide information concerning the diagnosis of illnesses being treated in U.S. hospitals. Eventually we conducted the project without their help, taking care to keep them informed of our study as it developed. We found that hundreds of Canadians were going to five American treatment centers that were close to the border, and a smaller number went to more distant U.S. facilities. We decided to concentrate on those five centers. We found that the Ontario government alone was spending millions of dollars to help pay for treatment costs incurred by Ontarians at these facilities, and we hoped that this statistic would help to convince the ministry to approve our future plans.

We had three related objectives in mind when we established Bellwood Health Services Inc. The first was to develop more specific treatment programs for patients addicted to alcohol, cocaine, and multiple drugs, which included more involvement of families (including children) and "concerned others." The second was to examine the feasibility of contracting with community hospitals to add addiction-treatment services to their other operations. The third, long-term objective was to broaden our program to address other lifestyle-related problems. We hoped eventually to promote total health for all age groups and thus to encourage individuals to resist the attractions of all forms of chemical abuse and dependence.

Linda and I were fully aware of the new difficulties that faced us. We needed all the help we could get, and I was relieved when a writer from *The Medical Post* contacted me in the summer of 1983 about an article he was writing on our plan to establish new services in Canada. We had just completed one survey on the U.S. treatment centers and what they were costing provincial governments, and the results, which he published, marked the beginning of widespread public support on our behalf. This included nationwide television and newspaper coverage, radio commentaries, and personal letters of petition from the public and from major corporations. Despite all this, the government of Ontario was not prepared to support new private operations in the addiction field, whatever the cost of the annual exodus of its citizens to private American institutions.

By the fall of 1983 the senior executives and other consultants had completed a five-year business plan for Bellwood. The next step was to find a broker to raise the money to carry out the plans. We were initially turned down by a couple of brokerage houses, but our lawyer, John Burns, introduced us to Bob Sale, then president of Walwyn, Stodgell, Cochran, Murray Ltd. Bob was very positive toward us and our concept. He turned to me and said simply, "You'll have your money, Doctor."

In January 1984 we met with the assistant deputy minister of health to discuss the possibility of purchasing the only private-hospital license then available in Ontario. Since the Ontario legislature had ceased to grant new licenses for private hospitals in the province, the only possible way Bellwood could obtain such a license was to buy an existing one if it became available. We awaited the ministry's reply, and sailed on with our plan to raise funds for Bellwood.

One of the investors' conditions for raising the money was that I obtain "key-man" insurance for two-and-a-half million dollars. We began working on it as soon as we learned of this condition for the private placement of our stock; we had been assured by a representative of an insurance firm that there would be no problem. We had not been told, however, that one of the conditions for receiving this insurance was that I must first pass a stress test. This presented me with a new challenge of some magnitude.

I reported for my stress test straight from work and in my usual business suit. Later, I was informed that I would have to undergo yet another test the next day for another insurance company. This time I arrived for the ordeal with a T-shirt, shorts, and running shoes, which certainly improved my performance. I had the weekend to rest up, thank heavens, because on the following Monday I had to take a third stress test for still another insurance company. I became very tense, because I did not know how many more I could handle, and we were faced with the possibility of losing the whole deal if I flunked out. My costs were already well over $35,000 and we had no idea of what the continuing legal bills and brokerage costs would be if the private placement did not succeed. "I expect to spend the rest of my working days paying off our debt," Linda told me, only half in jest.

In the meantime I came to my own conclusions. I decided that the insurance companies had a foolproof method of making money on their policies. Anyone who survived their stress tests without a coronary would probably live to be one hundred.

The suspense was relieved on Tuesday morning, March 13, when one of our insurance brokers, Dennis Toews, called to announce that he had been successful in arranging for all the key-man insurance. I owe thanks to Dr. Terry Kavanagh for teaching me how to stay in reasonable physical condition, and to Dennis Toews for making the entire life-insurance industry in North America aware of the seventy-two-year-old Canadian doctor who was looking for insurance coverage! Linda flew to Detroit that day and obtained the signature of William Clay Ford's lawyer. Bill Ford was one of Bellwood's investors, and we required the signature to close the deal.

We did close it on March 14 in our lawyer's boardroom.

The long hardwood table was covered with documents requiring signatures from Linda and me, and the signing process seemed to take forever. At the end I was presented with a check from Bob Sale for $2,010,000. I was overwhelmed! We were in business at last! Finally, we felt that major corporations and individuals in Canada had invested in a company to develop the latent resources of addicted people, just as they had always invested in mines, oil wells, and other natural resources. We rushed over to our downtown Toronto branch of the Royal Bank, where the manager was waiting after 5:00 P.M. to receive the deposit. With that amount of money we did not want to miss even one day of interest.

The good news did not last very long. We learned that our offer to purchase the private-hospital license had inexplicably been turned down, and we could not arrange a subsequent meeting with the owner. We returned to our plan of continuing negotiations with the public hospitals for contract services. Three of them expressed interest in such a relationship, and we developed further research plans and proposals with them. In the long run, however, none of them were prepared to submit a joint proposal to the Ministry of Health, since no comparable arrangement had ever been made between a public and a private agency in the addiction field. Once again we were forced to seek alternatives.

Along with all the other paths we had pursued during the previous year, we had spent time looking at various properties throughout Ontario with a view to operating a free-standing treatment facility on a fee-for-service basis, paying great attention to architectural, zoning, and other considerations. The Donwood Institute had been very generous in allowing us to continue to use space at the Northlea Church until the summer of 1984, when we had to find office space elsewhere. Fortunately, the Canadian National Institute for the Blind had some space available, which we were able to rent temporarily.

Our big break began with our discovery that adequate

space was available at Medical Inns, a multi-purpose health facility in the northeastern part of Metropolitan Toronto. We began discussions with the owner to rent space in his building, which housed a nursing home, retirement center, medical offices, and diagnostic laboratories. Not only did it have adequate space, it was properly zoned for a new residential clinical service. The building had originally been designed to function as a combined orthopedic-surgical hospital and hotel in which family members of the patients could stay while their loved ones were recuperating. This plan had also run afoul of the Ministry of Health, which refused to grant a private-hospital license for the operation. So we had to continue to seek approval from the Ministry of Health for our new treatment center, and hoped that we would soon be able to accommodate what we thought would be a long line of patients.

Following the finalization of our lease agreement with Medical Inns, we completed our proposal to the Ministry of Health for their funding. We based it on the same arrangements the ministry had with private American centers, which billed the ministry on a fee-for-service basis per patient.

We included relevant data to prove just how successful we had been over the years. In our submission we cited a follow-up study done by John McLachlan, Ph.D., of one hundred randomly chosen patients at Donwood during the mid-1970s. Fifty of them had been in the day clinic, and the other half had been admitted into the in-patient program. The results of the two groups were similar. Dr. McLachlan, who became director of psychology at Peel Memorial Hospital in Brampton, Ontario, reported in 1978 that seventy-four percent of the patients studied after two years, had shown significant improvement. The rest showed little or no improvement. His research also showed that there had been a significant increase in both the employment and employment-stabilization of these patients, and a marked reduction in their drinking on the job and absenteeism. Moreover, this study indicated an important improvement in the general physical, mental, and social well-being of those patients we had helped.

The McLachlan study was reported in clinical circles around the world and, we believed, helped support our argument for the need for more clinics based on the Donwood program. We also had every reason to believe that the statistics at Bellwood would reflect the same degree of success that the Donwood statistics did when Dr. McLachlan completed his research. We were prepared to provide the capital to set up the program, rent and furnish our facilities, hire and train the initial staff, and arrange a joint relationship with the ministry to cover our ongoing operations.

Premier William Davis announced his retirement in September 1984. The Progressive Conservatives had been in power for forty consecutive years, just a bit longer than I had been in the addiction-treatment field. I was worried by the news, because I suspected our fate would be left hanging indefinitely. My experience had been that civil servants were not disposed to make important decisions with the prospect of cabinet changes imminent.

In my dealings with the ministry, I continued to adhere to the same motto as that of the Holiday Inns hotel chain: "The best surprise is no surprise." In return for keeping the ministry informed of our plans through the years, I had always received co-operation and assistance from them even if I did not always get exactly what I wanted. I had followed the same routine in trying to put together the Bellwood package. There had been many meetings with various ministry officials over the previous two years, and many telephone conversations, but we never received an official acknowledgment of the receipt of our proposal. This surprised and annoyed me, but we continued with our plans to get Bellwood operational. We hired staff, made renovations in the Medical Inns building, and moved into the premises in October.

In mid-November, when we had still heard nothing from the ministry, I blew my stack. I called Clare Westcott, the executive director in Bill Davis' office, and told him how insulted I was that the Ministry of Health had not even had the courtesy to return my phone calls following our submission months before. As a result of my call, a meeting with senior ministry officials was quickly arranged for November 20.

The meeting provided us with a mixed bag of results. The officials were helpful, in spite of the atmosphere created by my having to go to Westcott with my complaints, and one of them suggested the possibility of our purchasing the private-hospital license I had been pursuing many months earlier. They also advised us to work with the ministry's community mental-health division in developing part of our program, which might qualify us for funding under that branch's guidelines.

We now focused our attention on satisfying the requirements of that division, but were unable to come up with a plan that could meet their criteria for funding. On their side, this division of the ministry seemed to feel no great urgency to discuss our proposals in great depth and respond to them quickly, possibly because their department was not the one paying the treatment bills to American addiction treatment centers.

By now we were admitting our first patients to Bellwood. The fact that the Medical Inns property housed a retirement home did not faze us, but it did startle a few of our first patients. One of them was a man from Winnipeg who had been rather inebriated when he spoke to us by phone to find out about our treatment plan. When he heard it was a five-year program, he arrived at Bellwood with his entire wardrobe. When he saw some of the nursing-home patients, he asked, "Is this what I'll be like after five years here?"

The man did stay for our twenty-eight-day, in-patient program. He also became typical of the patients who with our help together with continued support from groups like AA were able to overcome their dependence. When he eventually did get into trouble after his release from Bellwood, we advised him to attend an AA meeting every day for ninety days. Studies in the United States had shown that such a saturation program can help an alcoholic or drug addict absorb the philosophies propounded by the self-help groups. This particular patient went back to Winnipeg, got a good job, and regularly attended AA meetings. And he has stayed dry, even though there have been some traumatic experiences in his life, and he credits the support he has received from AA for his success in dealing with them.

Our first Bellwood patients were paying for their treatment in full themselves. Obviously, our services were available only to those individuals who could afford it, or who could have their treatment paid for by their employers. As a result, we were averaging three or four patients a month, and our capital was dwindling rapidly. I decided to try a slightly different approach to find the necessary funding.

I approached the Liquor Control Board of Ontario, which has the sole right to sell hard liquor and foreign beer and wine in the province, to ascertain the amount of money the board contributed to the treasuries of the province and federal government from their sales of alcoholic beverages. I concluded that the cost to the government of our patients' treatment, and the costs to society for the various problems associated with addiction, was far exceeded by liquor tax revenues to the provincial treasury. Alcoholics represented one class of patients which was contributing more to government coffers than the costs of their own treatment programs. Why not use at least part of those revenues, I asked, to fund treatment centers and prevention programs?

I sent my report under the title, "A New Approach to Payment for Treatment of Alcohol Abuse," to all the cabinet ministers in Ontario in January 1985. And although this same argument had been put forward by other concerned experts over the years, it drew no response from the appropriate government agencies. I was hardly surprised by the lack of a reaction.

Despite this and the other setbacks we had faced since getting Bellwood off the ground, I continued to believe that we would eventually succeed. And we received a boost in January from an unexpected source. Early that month, Linda attended an AA meeting in which one of our patients, Eleanor Townsend, received a medallion commemorating five years of sobriety, no mean accomplishment. Eleanor was then the only woman ever to win the North American Fiddling Championship. Eleanor had rewarded me for helping her achieve sobriety by composing a waltz for Mary and me. It was called "The Waltz of the Bells," and she has included it on one of her recordings.

Her brother, Jim Reid, a host reporter for the "W5" television program on CTV was also at the meeting, and he asked Linda how I was enjoying retirement. Linda replied that I was not in retirement at all, and briefed him on our current situation.

Jim asked, "Do you think there's a story in this?"

Linda said there was, and Jim began to research the details. As a result of this encounter, his story of our plight was first aired on "W5" in the spring and repeated later that summer. The television exposure certainly brought our situation into the limelight, and this new national awareness resulted in many letters of support for us being sent to the government from all over Canada. Gratifying as the favorable publicity was, however, it did not sit very well with the Ministry of Health. By now it faced pressure from influential people on all sides promoting provincial government funding for our addiction treatment center.

Our efforts received another friendly nudge at about the same time. In March I received a telephone call from a Mr. R. J. Moores, a vice-president and corporate secretary of the Royal Bank. He said he was calling to arrange an appointment for me to meet with him and Dr. Roger Gaudry, a former rector of the University of Montreal. Through the years I have received (and continue to receive) a number of calls from people asking to discuss in confidence a professional colleague or associate with an addiction problem. When I was asked to meet with a bank vice-president and former head of a major university, I assumed that a very important person indeed must be in some kind of serious trouble. We set a time for the meeting and Mr. Moores ended his conversation by saying, "Incidentally, it is good news."

Totally overlooking his last remark, I said, "Thank you very much. I look forward to seeing you," and I hung up the phone. It was only later that day that I began to think over the conversation, and to consider what kind of relationship there would be between Dr. Gaudry and Mr. Moores. I also wondered about how a discussion of an important person having a serious addiction problem could be considered good news. I was beginning to catch on, and to satisfy my suspicions I telephoned Mr. Moores in Montreal the next morning and said, "I'm just beginning to wake up to what you may have been talking about yesterday." Mr. Moores laughed at this and said, "I thought you took it very coolly!"

"I just can't believe it," I confessed with growing excitement, as I now understood the reason for the meeting. I was to receive the Royal Bank Award. Dr. Gaudry was chairman of the selection committee. When we met in my office a few days later, Dr. Gaudry told me that I was receiving a very prestigious award presented to only one person each year. Moreover, this important award was accompanied by a tax-free gift of $100,000 and a large gold medal!

For the three months before the presentation I was in a partial daze, but I was helped through the blitz of media interviews by the highly skilled public-relations department of the Royal Bank. The media constantly asked what I was doing, and the Bellwood story was repeated again and again in almost every news medium across the country. Unfortunately, all the publicity associated with the Royal Bank Award did not assist us in our negotiations with the ministry. There were simply too many political uncertainties in the province at the time for top ministry officials to make any major decisions.

The Royal Bank certainly knows how to throw a party! The award ceremonies helped take my mind off the still-growing financial crisis at Bellwood. My family and I were asked to compile a list of 200 guests, and the Royal Bank invited the same number. The Bellwood list included friends from my boyhood days, relatives, staff, friends, and a wide range of other associates. The dinner was held in June 1985 in one of the grand ballrooms at the Royal York Hotel in Toronto. It was one of the most enjoyable occasions of my life, despite the fact that the Bellwood situation was continually in the back of my mind. I shook so many hands I felt like a campaigning politician.

When my turn came to speak, I thanked the Royal Bank warmly, not only for the award and the spectacular affair that evening, but for their faith and help to us over the years. I noted that I had also been financially indebted to the Royal for almost thirty years before receiving the award. The loan that they had granted the Bell Clinic in November 1956 had saved our operation. The role played by the bank through a succession of prominent executives was critical — John Coleman, William Morison, and William Arthur all served at various times on the board of directors of the Donwood Institute. John Coleman had been chairman of the board when he arranged for a $300,000 line of credit for Donwood when it began its operations in 1967. The morale boost encouraged all of us associated with Bellwood to push on with our latest program. But the irony of the timing of the award was not lost on us.

The political situation in Ontario was unsettled due to an impending election. It wasn't until the Liberal party formed a minority government in Ontario in June 1985 that we finally had a health minister who was prepared to take action. Murray Elston had inherited our problems from the previous government and he was prepared to visit us to discuss the situation. Before his visit was arranged, a reporter for the *Toronto Star* came out to do a profile on me for the Royal Bank Award story. She spent a couple of hours with us, and enquired about Bellwood's current status. As a result, we received front-page coverage; my profile became secondary to the more newsworthy headline about the amount of money being spent by the provincial government for addiction treatment in the United States. Before Murray Elston had any opportunity to discuss our situation with us, he was assaulted with questions by the press about his ministry's inherited policy. To his credit he came out to Bellwood and promised us that he would look carefully into our predicament.

We hoped he would act quickly. It was now August 1985, and the funds we had obtained in March 1984 were quickly disappearing. We were still averaging three or four new patients a month who were receiving a very high level of individual care. Having four staff members for each patient led many people to wonder why we hadn't let some of the staff go in order to save money. The fact of the matter was that if we had laid off these highly qualified people, it would have taken months to gear up the operation again, and they might not have been available when we did need them. They were well trained, worked competently together as a team, and had become used to "shooting the rapids" with us. Nevertheless, we were forced to announce to them that we could not afford to pay them much longer, and that we would have to let them go. We were particularly sad, because these people had shared our dream with us, taken their own personal risks, and in spite of our collective difficulties, continued to maintain the high morale at Bellwood.

At the eleventh hour, however, we were saved by an unexpected turn of events. Since we had been told by the ministry that the private-hospital license we had sought was not available, we had totally given up hope of that possibility. Out of the blue, we were surprised by a phone call from its owner, who told us that the license was indeed for sale. Our spirits uplifted, we immediately contacted the Ministry of Health, which now confirmed that it would approve the license sale to Bellwood Health Services Inc. The ministry also said that it would be prepared to negotiate an annual global budget for us once the license had been transferred. I was at once astounded, bewildered, and ecstatic! There truly was a Santa Claus, and he had arrived early that year.

We completed the purchase on November 14, 1985, and then immediately negotiated a global budget with the ministry. This date was a mere three weeks prior to the day we had agreed we would have to begin shutting down Bellwood. It was a miracle of sorts, and it had occurred within three months of Murray Elston's visit to Bellwood. We had been through many difficult times before, but this was the closest we had ever come to ceasing operations completely. We had never before experienced so many frustrations, and at the same time, so much favorable publicity from the media and support from the business community. I was very pleased for my wife, Mary, and the rest of the family. Mary had endured years of hardship and uncertainty in the past, but she had never wavered in her support. Now she hoped that she could look forward to a time when such stressful situations would be only a distant memory.

Now that Bellwood was truly in business and soon running at full capacity, I felt that I had received the ultimate reward. But there was still one more to come. In the early fall of 1986 I received a call from Professor David Bell (a family friend but not a relative), who was then dean of the school of graduate studies at York University. He informed me that I had been selected to receive their honorary degree of Doctor of Laws at fall convocation a few weeks later. I did not have to inform the media about my troubles this time; the major problems all seemed behind me.

I fully enjoyed the ceremony at the university, as I sat impressively gowned on the platform with the faculty members. I completed my brief acceptance speech in the allotted time of ten minutes. The only sign that I might have been a little nervous occurred when I fumbled with my mortar-board while removing it for the national anthem. As the music ended, I proudly replaced it on my head — with the tassel hanging right in the middle of my forehead. As I gazed down from the platform, I could see a few of my family members trying to stifle their giggles.

As I suspected at the beginning of the 1980s, today we are treating a wide variety of addictions and cross-addictions, the most common being cocaine, alcohol, and a combination of the two. And while the reasons for developing a dependency may not have changed much over the years — rejection, loneliness, family background, for example — the types of addiction problems and the treatment techniques are certainly more sophisticated.

One of our recent patients, a young man, was addicted to cocaine and also used other drugs. He is the adult child of an alcoholic. One of his brothers died after an episode of mixing his addictions, and another has a dependency problem. Our patient had motivated himself to straighten out his life, but was unable to control his impulses. He could give up alcohol and cocaine, but not marijuana, and eventually he smoked enough to trigger a return to the other substances. After several attempts he finally completed our twelve-week, in-patient cocaine program. It appears that he has now found a road to recovery and a new life.

This young man is typical of the type of patient we now treat. We hope he will succeed, but there are many who won't, and the others confirm for me the need for institutions that confine their patients for up to a year in order to break their dependencies. Many consider our twelve-week, in-patient therapy program for cocaine addicts to be too long. We hear about athletes who have abused cocaine, spend thirty days in an addiction clinic, and then return to their teams. It appears, however, that many of them require a longer controlled introduction to recovery to succeed in overcoming their addiction. We believe that one month of in-patient care is not long enough when cocaine addiction is the problem.

We are constantly striving to improve our treatment methods, particularly where cocaine is involved. We now use laser acupuncture and drama therapy as parts of our program, and both appear to have made a positive impact. But some of our patients are showing us that we still have a long way to go.

"Robert" is a cocaine addict. He drank beer to come down from cocaine, which he had been smoking and snorting daily for eight months prior to his admission to Bellwood. He had also been using marijuana and hash regularly for twelve years. There was a history of chemical dependence on his mother's side. His year-old marriage to a woman who came from an alcoholic family was in trouble, and his job status was questionable. It appeared that he was dealing in drugs to support his thousand-dollar-a-week habit. He had no adult experience of working or of leading a social life without using a chemical. In fact, he had been a user from the age of twelve, which unfortunately is not that uncommon in many communities today.

Robert and his family appeared motivated to do something about changing his life, but he wanted to approach the recovery program on his own terms. He was very argumentative, hyperactive, and emotionally unstable, which is not unusual for our cocaine and cross-addiction patients. Robert went through the twelve-week, in-patient therapy program, but he had no patience for the Phase Three meetings and attended his drug-support group only if he had nothing else to do. A few weeks after his discharge, he relapsed, but said that his Bellwood experience had spoiled his enjoyment of cocaine. He encountered great difficulty in abstaining from THC (marijuana, hash), however, as it had been such an integral part of his life. He also had trouble breaking his social connections with his past, and struggled with the concept of honesty, which is so basic to a successful recovery. And then there was the temptation of the easy money he could make by dealing drugs, countered by the struggle to resist this lure in order to survive. He had some tough decisions to make.

Robert is working harder now at his recovery. He is beginning to realize that he cannot do it his way, is attending support meetings, and has become more open to accepting help and ideas from others. He appears to be maturing, but he still has a few mountains to climb, and the outcome is not yet certain.

What is certain is that we are seeing more and more patients like Robert, and that we not only have to work harder to develop better treatment methods, we must promote programs to prevent these addictions in the first place. To this end we have expanded in a number of directions to include families of our patients, paying special attention to the children, who are at high risk for developing the same addictions as their parents. We have also developed a residential treatment and follow-up service for adults who were raised in alcoholic homes. We provide assistance and counseling to families and employers concerned about someone resisting help for an alcohol or drug problem. In addition to our lifestyle-enrichment courses, we consider these programs a part of an integrated effort to promote health and the early recognition and prevention of all forms of chemical abuse.

When we set up Bellwood Health Services Inc., our intention was to provide total health-care programs and not just to treat addictions. Thus, I was interested when a neurologist, Dr. R. H. Wilson, in the Medical Inns building approached us in the fall of 1987 with the idea of our collaborating to establish a sleep-disorder clinic. We viewed the opportunity as the breakthrough we had been waiting for, the first non-addiction component of a total-health service. The doctors take the clinical responsibility for neurological assessments, and Bellwood provides the beds, nursing, and technical staff. In addition, we have developed treatment services for problems related to insomnia, including stress management, relaxation training, nutrition, and life-skills counseling. As I write, the hopes and challenges expressed in our choice of the name "Bellwood Health Services Inc." are beginning to be realized as we gradually expand in both purpose and recognition.

Expansion in these areas has been an answer in part to the question my patients have asked for years: "Why did I have to become an addict in order to learn about total health and a balanced lifestyle?" I remember listening to a provincial magistrate in 1947 when he thanked God that he had become an alcoholic. The experience had made him aware of all the things he was doing wrong, and how unfulfilled his life was.

Epilogue

Looking back over the years, one important point stands out very clearly. Our recovered patients have consistently played a major role in the financial support and planning of every stage of our development. Many have also made outstanding contributions to society after recovering from their addictions.

But I also vividly recall the many troubled patients we could not help. Some of the most brilliant, talented people I have known died in their prime due to illness or injury related to addiction, in spite of everything that we, AA, or other agencies could do. Although there has been remarkable progress in the understanding and management of chemical abuse and dependence since I first became involved over forty years ago, the global situation is far from reassuring. As I mentioned at the outset, we are fighting a war against an addiction problem that has reached pandemic proportions. As I also stressed, however, there is hope for the future.

As we enter the 1990s, there appears to be a rapid expansion of interest and concern about the global problems of chemical abuse and dependence. It is coming from all segments of the community — governments, professionals, educators, the courts, police, industry, and health-care agencies. There is a universal call for more information, more education, more treatment facilities, and more controlling legislation. But it is still the self-help groups, like the Fellowship of Alcoholics Anonymous, that lead the way in demonstrating that recovery from a dependence on alcohol or drugs is possible, provided that permanent abstinence from all mood-altering substances is maintained.

Recent research has demonstrated the nature and dynamics of the process that can expand dependence on chemicals beyond the range of control. Many new clinical approaches have also demonstrated that addiction is a treatable disability, and that the prospect of a new rewarding life, totally free of dependence on any potentially addicting chemicals can become a reality for the majority of victims.

We can win this war against chemical abuse and addiction. However, it will require the development of a more comprehensive, integrated effort by every member of all concerned communities than has been conceived or carried out before. Moreover, our concern with the human pollution of chemical abuse must be considered within the much broader context of the progressive pollution of our total global environment. We could work toward a global effort as more and more people concerned with our well-being and survival become involved. This objective must be able to transcend regional differences in government, religion, politics, race, and economic status.

Although science must be involved in guiding the direction of such a global effort, this would be only one part of the total operation. It is futile to expect that improved knowledge by itself can succeed in reducing experimentation with mood-altering substances by all age groups. It is also unrealistic to expect that we can win this war by controlling the supply of illicit drugs given the incalculable power of the forces promoting chemical abuse. In any event, supply is only one part of the equation. The motivation by an individual to maintain freedom from hazardous involvement with chemicals may be short-lived unless that person is given effective guidelines to achieve comparable feelings of general well-being. Current knowledge about the nature and development of total health programs can provide these guidelines. The challenge to society is to vigorously explore how to use our latent resources to achieve the states of total well-being that can compete effectively with the transient, recurrent, and dangerous joys of chemical abuse.

In my opinion, the reserves of adaptability in all people represent a combined power more than equal to the task of bringing about a global reduction in the demand for mood-altering substances. But we had better hurry. Studies done at Northwestern Hospital in Chicago indicate that permanent, even fatal damage can be done to a fetus if the mother has used certain drugs during pregnancy. Cocaine is particularly dangerous to the unborn child during the first three months of its development, a time when the mother is often unaware she is pregnant and may use it without thinking about the consequences.

As worldwide interest increases in the concepts of total health and wellness, we could take a lesson from the Fellowship of Alcoholics Anonymous. AA has demonstrated that its twelve-step program can transcend traditional racial, religious, and economic barriers. Why not a new fellowship, with a creed devoted to a balanced improvement in physical, mental, social, and spiritual well-being? Surely people of all countries, all cultures, and all religions can come together in co-operation for the fundamental purpose of survival. Can we not hope that this basic instinct common to all species can unite us in a joint effort to contain the manifold threats from all types of pleasurable chemicals?

In 1971 I had the good fortune to obtain a book entitled *Great Religions of the World*, published by the National Geographic Society. The foreword is by Krister Standahl, dean and professor of divinity, Harvard Divinity School, and editor of the *Harvard Theological Revue*. Krister Standahl points out that man's gradual shift from hunting, fishing, and the gathering of wild fruit, grains, and vegetables to agriculture, manufacturing, shopkeeping, and commerce made it necessary for him to modify or abandon his traditional ruthless reaction to all strangers. As Dr. Standahl points out, "[man] had to learn how to behave toward other people he did not know." Standahl also stressed that the message of helping one's fellow man — the Golden Rule — is contained in the creed of six major world beliefs: Christianity, Judaism, Islam, Buddhism, Hinduism, and Confucianism.

We are now faced with the most critical global crisis of all time — is it not possible that the ground rules for its solution, through a caring worldwide community, were established long ago?